3

Villiard, Paul
Moths and how to rear them. N.Y., Funk & Wagnalls [c1969] 10.00
242 p. illus.

1. Moths. 2. Insects-Collection and preservation. I. t

MOTHS
AND HOW TO
REAR THEM

MOTHS
AND HOW TO
REAR THEM

Paul Villiard

Funk & Wagnalls

NEW YORK

To *Gertrude, Paul Jr.,* AND *William*

Preface

This book was compiled to offer the person interested in rearing moths—for whatever reason—information on foodplants, alternate foods, overwintering conditions, rearing requirements, equipment, and other pertinent knowledge which is unfortunately lacking to a great degree in publications in the United States.

While Europe, the British Isles and the Orient—particularly Japan—have great numbers of rearers of butterflies and moths who are encouraged in many ways, the negative attitude of our Department of Agriculture puts such a dampener on the activity in this country that the dissemination of knowledge, distribution of breeding stocks, and the accumulation of important biological and ecological data become most difficult.

Perhaps this restriction is the cause of such a dearth of literature on the subject. Be that as it may, there is not one really comprehensive manual for breeders published in the country, with the exception of the Collins and Weast book on silkmoths, which contains excellent information on a limited number of species.

The fact that most of the species being reared and studied are tropical and subtropical and entirely unable to withstand the rigors of our winter conditions has nothing to do with the case in the eyes of the U. S. D. A. The simple fact that the species is non-indigenous is enough to condemn it by these unenlightened guardians of our forests. All this is the result of some specimens of *Porthetria dispar*—Gipsy moths—being liberated sometime in the middle 1800's by an entomologist who should have known better. Granted, the Gipsy moths have taken over and nearly defoliated large tracts of forest lands in the eastern states. Nonetheless, breeders today are more aware of the danger of liberating foreign species which would be able to cope with our climate and which would accept foodplants native to the United States. The reason the Gipsy moths obtained such a foothold in this country is that they will eat practically any plant whatever and there is no natural predator here to keep them in check. As a result, they run rampant—eating everything in their path—with disastrous results to our forests.

In the light of what has happened with this species, the U. S. D. A. is entirely justified in blocking the entry of any species which could survive. Certainly, however, they should allow the importation of tropicals and exotics which have not the slightest chance of surviving a winter or of gaining a foothold in this country. That they draw the line so completely and indiscriminately shows a singular tendency toward tunnel-vision.

No attempt has been made to make this a complete breeder's manual, with the inclusion of all available species. This would be a lifework of many volumes. Rather, selection has been made of representative species from the genera which are most readily available throughout the realm of rearers and breeders.

Foodplants and special requirements such as temperature, humidity, etc., are stated, and enough general information is given so that the breeder can easily rear a brood of whatever species takes his fancy. Worldwide genera are included, and eggs from one or another of each genus can always be obtained in any one season. Sometimes several seasons go by without certain species being offered for sale. This is due to rarity, loss of bloodlines in a breeder's stock, or blanket-spraying wiping out races in large areas. For some years the lovely *Graelsia isabella* of Spain has been unavailable due to spraying and, indeed, it is feared that the race was so sharply depleted that the species is in great danger of total extinction.

More than seven years have gone into the preparation of this volume, which, I think, will be the first breeder's manual on moths to be published in the United States.

Much had to be learned before the manuscript could be written. At the beginning we were unable to recognize foodplants, and many weeks would be spent in trying to identify certain plants, trees, and shrubs in order to make certain the supply of a foodplant for a given species.

Finally woods acreage was purchased, which then had to be cleared and re-planted for the required foods. Water had to be provided, so a well was dug; shelter was supplied for our caterpillars as protection from the elements and from predators. Slowly our "Butterfly Farm" came into being. After the years of toil and construction and because it is situated well back off the road, we have fondly renamed it "Back Achers."

Then began the research into all the ramifications of rearing moths. We simply *had* to learn trees and shrubs, so much of our time was devoted to the study of botany and dendrology. Gardening came in for more time. In order to grow the plants we had to install sprinkling systems and, since we were on the farm only one day each week, these systems had to be automatically operated by the use of electric solonoid valves and time clocks. A cabin was erected, then added to. A well house was built and cages constructed for housing our charges.

We drove all over the eastern seaboard to nurseries, searching out specimen plants that were not in regular nursery stocks. These we brought back and lovingly tended on our farm.

Most of the difficulty with the foodplants arose from the inability to identify the species needed in the winter twig. This is the time you must be able to recognize the food for overwintering ova, since in the very early spring the tropical and oriental species hatch out long before our trees are in bud. Branches must therefore be brought inside and forced in the warmth of the home in vases of water, and, unless you know the trees, you do not know where to look for the food.

All the information we have amassed is now presented to you, with the hope that it will lessen the work for you and allow one short step forward in the accumulation of knowledge in this most interesting branch of science.

Elsewhere in the book you will find a whole section devoted to photographs of winter twigs of various trees and shrubs, for your identification, so the time lost by us in learning these things will be saved from now on by newcomers to the field of endeavor.

A handy ready-reference index of foodplants for the individual species is also included, to save time reading the individual life histories in order to determine what foods you must have available for any given species of moth.

Every specimen in this book was reared by us in order to gain firsthand knowledge of what the species required in the way of food, shelter, temperature, humidity, etc. Every specimen was photographed by me to illustrate this volume, except the half-dozen or so that are indicated as having been supplied by other breeders.

This has been a difficult book to write, and a rewarding one. I have been made to realize that I have tapped a branch of science in which there is an astonishing amount of work still to do. It is my very real hope that this book will start others on the road toward doing some of that work, and that their findings may be made available to still other groups after them. Only by step-by-step progress can we finally arrive at some of the answers to questions which now baffle us.

I have become very humble in assessing the seven years of knowledge I have accumulated in the preparation of this volume. I know now much that I did not know before, and I know, really, nothing about the field, having made the merest scratch in it. It is my intention to continue with the research and eventually write an advanced manual. Certainly there is room for many books on the subject, and perhaps this one will give impetus to some other ambitious writers who will help share the load of dissemination of knowledge on the subject.

This book is not intended as a scientific text dealing with classification or identification of species. It is designed solely as a guide for amateurs and professionals who wish to raise moths as a hobby, for sale, or as a source of perfect specimens for their collections. No attempt has been made to follow any entomological order of presentation other than to group together all specimens belonging to the same family: e.g., the Saturniidae, Noctuidae, Sphingidae, etc., are discussed as separate groups.

Directions are also given for the construction of cages, sleeves, and other simple equipment used in the rearing of moths, and space is devoted to the photography of the insects in their different stages, with a discussion of photographic equipment used in the illustration of this book.

Acknowledgments

I would like to express my heartfelt thanks and appreciation to the many friends and acquaintances who have helped me toward the completion of this book. Particular thanks are due to Mr. Duke Downey of Sheridan, Wyoming; Mr. Paul E. Stone of Munith, Michigan; Mr. Robert Weast, co-author with Mr. Michael M. Collins of *Wild Silkmoths of the United States;* and Mr. Max Richter of East Durham, New York, for the help given in making available material which otherwise would have been most difficult to obtain.

Much help and material was also supplied by Mr. Brian O. C. Gardiner of Cambridge, England; Mr. Robert C. Gooden of Worldwide Butterflies Ltd., in Over Compton, England; Mr. Otto Jancik of Furth, Austria; and so many other generous and able rearers in this country and abroad that to list them all here would make this volume look like a roster of lepidopterists instead of a breeder's manual.

Particular thanks must go to my long-suffering wife, who, from having a horror of creatures like caterpillars some two and a half decades ago, has come to admire them, and whose unflagging devotion and untiring labor in feeding, cage cleaning, and all the other drudge jobs that go into the making of a book, have lightened my burden immeasurably, and, indeed, made the work possible.

And to my son William whose prodigious labor in concrete work, grading, excavating, plumbing, wiring, carpentry, and all the other skills necessary to build our butterfly farm in Upper New York State was freely and cheerfully given. Indeed, the work early became a family project, with my wife and son taking on the burden of routine to free me for the actual writing and the photographing of the living specimens.

Thanks to our older son Paul Jr. who each time home from his tours of duty overseas would pitch in to pull his share of the load.

Special thanks are due to the Honeywell Photographic Company in Denver for generously making available the equipment used for the critical photography of ova as shown in this volume. All but a very few of these pictures were taken with a Honeywell Pentax Spotmatic, Model H3v or H1a camera, fitted with bellows and a special Bellows-Takumar lens, Macro-Takumar, or the standard Super-Takumar on a reversal ring. The illumination was supplied by a Honeywell Prox-O-Lite, and in some cases with the Auto Strobonar/660 light.

Mr. Robert S. Bryant, of Baltimore, Maryland, was most generous in sending material for use in the rearing of several species, and many hours were spent by Mr. Paul W. Beard, of Monterey, California, collecting eggs in the wild of the western species, notably *Hemileuca nevadensis.*

PAUL VILLIARD

Saugerties, New York

Contents

MOTHS
AND HOW TO
REAR THEM

General Rearing Instructions

The equipment used to rear moths need not be very complicated. An enclosure of some kind is needed for each species: a cage if indoor rearing is to be undertaken; a sleeve or larger cage if the caterpillars are to be raised outdoors on living plants. The enclosure should be as roomy as possible, within your limits. I use three standard sizes of cages for outdoor purposes, and one for indoor rearing. To start the tiny first-instar larvae, plastic sandwich boxes or the small covered plastic boxes about three inches by five inches and two inches deep that are available in most dime stores and supermarkets do very nicely.

For the next one or two instars, depending on the amount of larvae and their size, a brooder made from a coffee can and a Coleman lamp chimney is ideal. These are very easy to make. You need a standard one-pound coffee can and a lamp chimney obtainable in most hardware stores or sporting goods stores that sell camping equipment. The size chimney to get is Coleman #660 Clear. Coffee cans and this particular chimney seem to have been designed to go together, because the chimney is an exact fit inside the rim of the coffee can lid. A hole should be cut in the center of the lid to accommodate a large cork—preferably rubber—through which a one-half-inch hole has been drilled. The inside of the lid and the inside of the can should be given a coat of Rustoleum to prevent corrosion.

The use of this brooder is simplicity itself. You fill the can with water to within an inch of the top, put on the lid with the cork stuck into the hole, push the sprigs of foodplant through the cork into the water, plugging the spaces around the stems with a bit of cotton or paper towel, and set the chimney over all, making

Coffee-Can Brooder If the foodplants are tall, like privet, two lamp glasses may be stacked and fastened together with masking tape. Always note the hatching date of the larvae

certain that the chimney is fitted inside the rim. Fasten a square of cheesecloth over the top with a rubber band, and presto! you have a perfect small cage.

As your charges outgrow the brooders you should have a cage ready that is large enough to carry the lot through to maturity. A useful size for these cages is eighteen by twenty-two inches, and sixteen inches high. Two frames are made of one by two lumber which is grooved on one edge to accept a sheet of one-eighth-inch masonite. The back is of this masonite, and the ends are double strength window glass, as is the front, which slides back and forth in the groove to open or close the cage. The top is a piece of one-half-inch thick plywood which has had

4

the center cut out to make a frame which is covered with screening. The whole assembly can be held together by screwing three screw-hooks into the top and the bottom frame and snapping a screen door spring between each pair of hooks.

The assembly should be stood on a base made of three boards nailed to a piece of plywood into which are bored several holes. The boards should be wide enough to lift the base as high as is required to slide a large jar underneath for holding the water. The foodplants are stuck through the holes in the base into the jars of water. As the brood grows larger, additional jars may be slid underneath the base and more holes filled with food. Of course, if you are not using all the holes at the same time, the extra ones should be covered with a stopper or square of cardboard laid over to keep the animals from escaping.

For rearing outdoors, sleeves pulled over leafy branches are the most commonly used method of containing the brood. The smallest practical size would be two lengths of fiberglass screening one yard wide and six feet long, to all ends of which is sewn a one-yard length of tough material such as unbleached muslin.

The two composite lengths are then put together and stitched down the sides to make a long tube, which is then turned inside out and flat stitched again to lock the seams. In use, a branch is selected that is well-leafed out and shaken severely to free it from any predators that may be hidden among the twigs. The sleeve is pulled over the branch until the material end of the sleeve is clear of the leaves on the branch, at which point it is tied securely to the branch at the trunk end. After putting the stock on the leaves, the terminal end of the sleeve is tied securely also, and the total effect is that of a cage around the branch.

Each day the terminal end of the sleeve should be opened and the accumulated frass and refuse dumped out. Watch that no predacious insects fly into the sleeve while you have it open. It is a good rule never to open a sleeve or outdoor cage alone, but to always have a helper around who can watch the opening for you while you are occupied with the cleaning.

Sleeves can be made in almost any size. I have several that are ten feet long and four feet wide, with two-yard ends—an imposing total length of twenty-two feet! It is a real task to get it over an enormous branch ten or fifteen feet up in the air. These giant sleeves are needed only when rearing very large batches of larvae, or when you must leave them without attention for a long period of time when, otherwise, they would starve to death before you returned to attend to them.

Another way of confining the animals outdoors is to make large cages which will enclose an entire small tree or shrub. I use three standard sizes of outdoor cage. The smallest one is for shrubs such as honeysuckle, lilac, viburnum, etc., and is thirty inches square and forty-eight inches high. The middle-sized one will cover a young tree, or an older one that is topped to keep its growth down, and measures three feet square and six feet high. The last and largest cage is four feet square and eight feet high, with a one-foot base, making the total height nine feet. This is about the largest practical size that can be used in a cage because the resistance offered to the wind would make the anchoring a large task. As it is, all cages should be very well anchored by leaning a concrete block on the bottom rail of each side. Sand is shoveled around the bottoms of the cage after it is in place to keep small animals and insect predators from gaining access. Even then, a Bembix wasp or other sand-boring predator might gain access once in a while and take its toll of the occupants.

As the broods are growing up in your cages, attention must be given to the time when they will be ready to pupate, and provision made for their needs. Sphingid moths, for the most part, burrow underground before pupating and, unless you allow them to go underground in an outdoor cage (leaving the cage in place all winter until they emerge in the spring), you must make a place for them to exercise this proclivity. A box eighteen inches wide, three feet long, and from eight to ten inches deep is a good size. It should be fitted with a tight, screened cover, and several holes bored through the bottom and screened to allow drainage without the burrowing caterpillars escaping.

The box should be fitted with a mixture of one part sand, one part sifted topsoil or loam, and two parts ground or chopped peat moss, all well blended. When the caterpillars show signs of wanting to pupate, they should be placed in the box and the cover put in place. They will burrow down as far as they like and undergo their metamorphosis. After caterpillars are placed in a pupating box they should not be disturbed for at least three weeks. Even better, the box should be left undisturbed through the entire diapause. In the case of exotics and tropicals, the box could be brought into the house for storage in the basement or other cool area. For those species indigenous to this country or which are able to withstand the local winter temperatures, the best thing is to put the box in a sheltered place outside and let it go through the winter under natural conditions. If there are enough drain holes in the bottom and they are well screened, the pupae will not drown when it rains or when the snow melts, and predators will be unable to enter and attack the pupae.

It would be helpful for the beginner to become acquainted with some useful information pertaining to breeding all species and to general management and methods.

Moths and butterflies belong to that group of insects which undergo *complete metamorphosis,* i.e., four separate and distinct stages: ova, larva, pupa, and adult or imago. The egg or ova stage is much the easiest to start with. These are obtained in many different ways. Local species are often attracted to a strong light placed outdoors in summer evenings. The so-called "black light" is the most effective, but an ordinary fluorescent lamp will pull in hundreds of night flyers. Not all will be useful, and the majority will be males, but many females will also be attracted and these will very often be gravid and will lay eggs for you if placed in a paper sack or a shoe box and left undisturbed for a day or two. Of course you must identify the species and be able to obtain its foodplant.

Purchased from another breeder or a dealer in living material, the eggs are generally sent inside a goose quill stoppered with a tuft of cotton. This quill is dropped into an airmail letter to shorten the transit time to you.

Lepidopterous insects overwinter in all four of their stages, and sometimes you will obtain eggs that overwinter either late in the summer or early in the fall when the adults pair. These should be put into small plastic boxes and labeled well.

The boxes may then be stored in the refrigerator—*not in the freezer*—until the next spring.

Plastic zipper boxes are ideal containers for eggs, and may be had gratis from stores that install zippers and sell notions.

Ova which are unfertilized collapse a few days after being laid and slowly shrivel up, while viable ova remain plump and full. Some species normally have an indentation in the shell, and this does not mean the egg is infertile.

Eggs do not tolerate too much shaking around, so roll them about in the storage box as little as possible. It is a good idea to try to get eggs from those breeders who actually breed the species, not from persons who buy wholesale then re-distribute in smaller quantities, since the rigors of transportation are hard on the ova. One airmail trip does not seem to do them too much harm, but by the time they have gone half-way around the world to the breeder, stored for an indefinite amount of time, then repacked and sent off again to you, the poor things give up and many fail to hatch when the time arrives. Also, they should be packed in the quill just tightly enough so that they do not roll around all the time they are in the plane. The wad of cotton should touch the last ova in the quill but not jam them all tightly together. This is because often eggs hatch while in transit and the caterpillars have a hard enough time living until you can free them, without being squashed in the bargain. Ova should be removed from the quill immediately upon arrival and put into a labeled box for storage and/or hatching. It goes without saying that each species is kept separate from all other species, and, if there is a considerable amount of time to pass before hatching, it is a good idea to put the names of the foodplants on the label along with the name of the species.

Have a plastic brooder box available for each species you intend to hatch. When the caterpillars begin to leave the shell, rarely will all of them hatch at the same time. The baby caterpillars should be left in the hatching box for at least half a day before transferring them to the brooder box in order to give them time to eat some of their egg shell if they so desire. Some species require part of the shell as their first meal, and *Stauropis fagi* will die if removed from the shell, since for the first several days it feeds on nothing else.

In transferring the tiny larvae to the brooder box, they should be picked up very gently with the soft bristles of a camel's hair water-color brush, carried over the brooder, and allowed to walk off the brush onto the leaves of the foodplant. Do not try to pull or wipe the caterpillar off the brush. Some of them hold on so tightly to their support that you will literally pull the legs off them or pull their bodies in two before they will release their grip. Enormous patience is needed as you work with the little animals. For that matter, patience in huge proportions is the prime factor in rearing, and if you do not possess it in practically unlimited amounts, it is my sincere recommendation that now is an excellent time to donate this book to a friend or to your public library and to forget about it.

After all the hatched larvae have been transferred to the foodplant, cover the box carefully and put a label on the box—not on the lid, because lids can be mixed up too easily—and put the box with the unhatched eggs on top of the lid.

At least twice a day look to see if any more eggs have hatched, and keep transferring the hatchlings to the foodplant.

Never put the unhatched eggs into the boxes with the foodplants. Cut leaves give off carbon dioxide, and if the eggs are put into the same box they might suffocate in the carbon dioxide gas before they hatch.

The food must be changed daily or, in some extreme instances where the plant wilts rapidly, twice daily. The baby larvae must not be forcibly removed from the food to be put into the fresh lot. Rather, a bit of leaf with the caterpillar on it is snipped off and laid onto a fresh leaf. The caterpillar will walk onto the new leaf when he gets hungry enough. When you cut the bit of leaf, be careful to look on both sides before snipping. It is very easy to miss another caterpillar on the bottom, with the result that you transfer one-and-a-half caterpillars to the fresh food.

Generally the larvae will molt into the second instar within a week or less after hatching. The caterpillar spins a pad of silk on a leaf or other support. This pad is very hard to distinguish when you are a beginner because it is so tiny. The caterpillar attaches his claspers to the pad so that he has a purchase from which to pull out of his old skin. This is one of the main reasons why, when transferring caterpillars to fresh food, you should not pick them up with the brush or pull them off their leaf. If you cut around them, enough of the pad will be left to afford a purchase and the molt will continue normally.

Just before, during, and just after the molt the animal is most vulnerable. On no condition should it be handled or subjected to drafts or sudden changes of temperature or humidity. When it starts feeding again it is on the road to hardening up and soon thereafter may be treated normally with no danger. Some species of caterpillars remain in a torpid state for several days before molting. They do not feed (or at most, only sporadically), and they should not be handled or disturbed.

Many species eat all or part of their shed skins. As a general rule, the fleshy naked larvae are skin eaters and the hirsute, urticating species are not. In any event, the cast skin should be left in the cage with the caterpillars for at least a full day before removal. If the old skin remains on the second day it is safe to assume that the caterpillar has no intention of eating it, and it may be discarded.

Caterpillars caged indoors should never be placed in direct sunlight, since they are not cooled by moving air and might easily suffocate in the built-up heat in the cage. Outdoors the sun is not such a hazard, since the breeze is constantly changing the air within the cage or sleeve, and the caterpillar may walk to the underside of the leaf to escape the direct rays.

Certain species of larvae will withstand crowding without too much discomfort. *Automeris io*, for instance, will live under conditions that would quickly kill another species. On the other hand, *Aglia tau* simply cannot tolerate a heavy population density and will expire if it is too crowded.

Some kinds need a dry, moderately cool atmosphere for their well-being, and others want it very humid, if not actually wet. *Antheraea mylitta* is one which requires a great deal of moisture. Their food, themselves, and the interior of their cage should be sprayed with tepid water at least once a day and preferably two or three times daily.

Many species of caterpillars are night feeders and, when first hatched, will wander all over the box or cage without feeding. It is a good practice to cover each brooder box or cage with some sort of light shield for the first few days, until you see that the baby larvae are feeding well. After the first molt the cover can be discarded, and the larvae will remain on the foodplant during the daytime even though they do not feed until dark.

It is a good idea to simulate as nearly as possible the natural photoperiod, e.g., when the day normally ends, cover the cage, and in the early morning remove the light barrier. Within limits, it is possible to accelerate the growth of caterpillars by lengthening their normal feeding period—artificial daylight if they are light feeders, or extended covering of the cage if they feed normally at night.

The "rate of living" varies considerably among individuals of the same brood, and this rate of growth is directly proportional to the temperature and the amount of fresh food available. In every brood there will be some runts, and generally these are still quite small caterpillars when the remainder are spinning their cocoons or preparing to pupate. Quite often the runts expire without completing their growth. There are many reasons for this stunting of individuals. A common one is not observing if the larvae are night or day feeders when they hatch. The little caterpillars spend all their time wandering about instead of feeding at this critical time in their growth.

Another cause is not realizing that the larvae are ready to molt, and pulling them off their silk pad and thrusting them onto the fresh leaves where, being unable to find a support to shed their skins, they must perforce wander about before eventually spinning or attempting to spin a new pad. More often they die in their old skin.

Then there are the occasional specimens which do not feed well from the very start, and for no apparent reason. These may be unwell—perhaps they are lacking the chemical stimulus to feed that is normal to their kind. Whatever the reason, these specimens are far behind the rest of the brood and are really a bother to care for, especially after the others have pupated. It seems a pity to kill them or otherwise dispose of them just because they are backward in growing, but certainly they must not be released in the wild under any circumstances. Regardless of the fact that almost certainly they will be eaten by birds or other predators, *the release of any non-indigenous species is the cardinal sin of a breeder.*

A very well known cause of stunting is the use of cut food instead of growing foodplants. In an article of mine which appeared in the April 1964 issue of *Natural History* magazine, this effect was described in some experiments made with the Indian Moon Moth, *Actias selene.* To quote from the article, "The results obtained with *Actias selene* were even more dramatic, because they were reared on an alternate foodplant in an unnatural climate. Apple was used, and because the tree was very large I resorted to sleeving individual branches, rather than topping and caging the entire tree.

"Again, leaves from the same tree were used to feed the indoor brood, which showed a marked tendency toward stunting, and which pupated at a much smaller size, and about ten days earlier than those on the tree outdoors. This seemed to indicate an adaption to adverse conditions, because the cut food dried out considerably during the day, with the result that for much of the time the

9

caterpillars fed on hard leaves, or on scraps that had fallen to the bottom of the cage. The accumulation of frass in the bottom of the cage also created a condition not found in natural surroundings. The lack of sunshine and circulating air, and the artificial photoperiods all were contributing factors toward the total condition.

"The early pupating time could thus be seen as an escape from these conditions. Typical specimens showed great differences in size after emergence. From the growing tree, average males measured 13.3 cm. across the forewings and 12.8 cm. from the tip of the forewing to the bottom of the hind wing processes. The cage-reared specimens spanned 9.3 cm. across the wings and only 8.7 cm. from top to bottom."

While the above was an excellent example of the advantages of fresh food against cut leaves indoors, not all species will respond so dramatically and, to some of the more hardy kinds, the mere fact that they have food is all that interests them, and they will do well anywhere they can eat their fill. However, it makes for much more consistently healthy animals if freshly cut food in abundance is offered to them.

When the caterpillar reaches the time of imminent pupation, it generally evacuates its intestines in the form of a squirt of dark liquid; if the caterpillar ejects this onto the leaves, the soiled ones should be removed as soon as you see them and not be allowed to remain until another caterpillar eats them.

Some species, after cleaning themselves out, start to restlessly run about the cage. This is especially noted in some of the *Lasiocampidae*, who are veritable racehorses and who gallop around the perimeter of their cage literally making a path in the accumulated debris on the bottom. It is at this time that you must be prepared with whatever they need for pupation. A box for Sphinx larvae, leaves for io and luna moths, and leafy branches for the big *Antheraea* larvae, for instance.

Many kinds of caterpillars, notably the naked ones, change color just before pupation. This is very noticeable in the *Brahmaea* group; *Brahmaea japonica* turns a deep chestnut brown on the entire dorsal surface just before going underground. Many of the *Antheraea* change their color, losing their vividness and becoming muddy and dull. *Rothschildias*, which have white stripes on their sides, generally change the stripes to orange or at least darken them. All of these indications are excellent time-clocks for the breeder and serve to announce that the time of pupation is here.

At times, every breeder will obtain species that are new to him and to his friends as well. Nothing may be known about the requirements or what foodplant is acceptable. When this challenge arrives, it calls for ingenuity and common sense. You know that you are going to lose most of your stock. Perhaps the first time it happens you will lose it all. Remember that you have, at most, two days in which to find their food or an alternate which is acceptable. The safest way is to divide your hatchlings into groups of two or three. Make up brooders with bouquets of three or four different foodplants in each, and place one group of larvae in each brooder. Watch very closely to see if any one caterpillar starts to feed *eagerly* on any of the leaves. It is common for a caterpillar to take a nibble out of an otherwise unacceptable leaf, so be sure that they are actually feeding before you put all of them on that particular foodplant.

The great standby foodplants and the ones that are accepted by the greatest number of larvae from all over the world are privet, walnut, hickory, cherry, lilac, oak, willow, apple, plum, and hawthorn. These should be the first tries, then go on to the less often used foods; the main thing is to try *everything* you can lay your hands on. In attempting to find the foodplant for *Argema mittrei*, for instance, I offered a total of nearly fifty different plants, to no avail. Finally, the last two larvae left alive accepted and grew fat and happy on—poison ivy!

Often, especially when you get eggs from other countries, they will arrive very early in the spring and, to your dismay, start to hatch before the leaves are out. This happens all too often, and it is a terrible thing to have to watch the helpless animals crawl about hungrily searching for food, finally expiring from the lack of it. A good practice when you have ordered eggs that may hatch early is to make a trip to the food tree and cut a good supply of branches with the largest buds on them. These can be put into a container of water and the leaves forced in the warmth of the house. In a week or two the buds should begin to open; the young larvae can then eat the opened buds and survive until the leaves open outdoors. This early hatching is a real problem, and it is most often found in African species where the seasons are reversed, or partly reversed from ours. A good idea, when possible and where practical, is to have a stock of small trees or shrubs in wooden tubs as starter plants. These tubs can normally live outdoors, but in the very early spring may be brought into the comparative warmth of a sheltered porch, or even indoors if space permits. They will leaf out much earlier than their counterparts in nature, and you will thus have a good supply of fresh food for early hatchers.

Bear in mind that when tiny, the caterpillars eat comparatively very little food. They grow rapidly, however, and the amount of food needed increases as they grow. A branch upon which twenty-five or thirty caterpillars in their first skin could live a week—until they were ready to molt—would last the same number of caterpillars only two or three days after the molt, and would suffice for only a day's food for two or three caterpillars from the same brood when in their third or fourth instar! For this reason, if branches are being forced, it is good insurance to start new batches at intervals of two or three days to assure an unbroken continuity of leaves for the increasing appetites of the growing larvae.

It is at this time, too, that thought must be given to the population density of your colony. The brooder or cage that accommodated them all in the beginning can be very quickly overcrowded to the point of danger if the caterpillars are allowed to grow out of room. Except for species which cannot tolerate crowding at all, and which must be kept in small groups from the very beginning, it is common practice to start an entire group in the same brooder, but to divide them into smaller lots or to transfer them to larger cages as they mature. Some of the *Antheraea* larvae get to look almost like sausages, as do some of the *Rothschildias*. Our domestic *Cecropia* caterpillar is enormous, and not over six or eight of them should be put into a six-foot sleeve.

Always wash the leaves of cut food well, and shake them dry before offering them to your caged specimens. In the confinement of a comparatively small cage, with a limited amount of food, any dirty leaves, soiled by bird droppings, insect exudation, or similar contaminants, must necessarily be eaten along with the rest of the food. On a caged tree, the chance of the caterpillar eating soiled leaves

11

drops quite markedly, until it is of relative unimportance. Then, too, there is the possibility of the leaves being washed clean by the rain.

Diseases are much more apt to break out in cage-reared broods than batches reared outdoors, but an epidemic can rage through a cage or a sleeve decimating or entirely eliminating the colony. Not too much can be done to save any members of a brood if disease does break out. The best thing to do is to segregate that entire colony from any others you may be rearing, and to clean and sterilize the cage or the sleeve as soon as the last member is removed. Cages should be very carefully scoured out after every rearing, even though there was no sickness. All parts should be first cleaned of any adhering dirt, then washed well with ammonia and allowed to dry for a day before using again. If the cage can be dried in the direct sunlight, so much the better. If an outbreak of disease has occurred, the cage should be washed after the ammonia with water-soluble Terramycin dissolved in hot water and allowed to dry in the sun.

Another method of cleaning a cage is to wash it thoroughly with a five percent solution of baking soda, to which is added a little detergent. This method, recommended by Mr. Brian O. C. Gardiner of Cambridge, England, is excellent because the diseases decimating a brood are generally caused by a virus, the spores of which can remain infective for several years! They also become resistant to most of the disinfectants used for killing bacteria. Alkaline solutions destroy them effectively, and a solution such as that above is easily made and easily used. You should make certain that all corners, cracks, and crevices are well saturated with the chemical, and soaking the parts of the cage should be achieved if possible.

The rearing of moths which hibernate in their larval phase, such as *Arctiidae,* can be a hazard, because it is difficult to set up an artificial ecological condition that will protect the caterpillars from freezing and allow them to awaken and browse on unusually warm days, as is their wont.

If you have grounds on which you can build a place for the special rearing of these kinds of caterpillars, it is a comparatively simple matter. The space should be quite large in area—certainly not less than six feet wide and eight feet long. A divider grid can be made to fit inside that will section off the area into two-foot by three-foot spaces, and screens made to fit together to cover the entire top. A section of screen can be removed if desired, for access to the interior. The whole affair need not be high. A one-inch by twelve-inch board would be fine for the sides, with the screens on top of them. The grid to support the smaller screens could be made of one-inch by six-inch lumber, set in flush with the tops of the sides. The caterpillars would have ready access to the entire area under the grid. The soil upon which the cage is erected should be well-packed and level. The entire area should be planted to dandelion, plantain, and dock, and the plants should be established for a season before you use it for rearing. Piles of rocks, a few lengths of log—with the bark left on—and small sections of waterproof exterior plywood about a foot square could be laid directly on the ground to afford a shelter under which the larvae could crawl. In other words, try to make a waste area replica of a small section of a vacant lot, even to a few empty cans, which make ideal hideouts for small things and hold heat well. Piles of pine needles or dry leaves can be scattered around in the corners. All these places make shelter areas in which or under which the hibernating caterpillars can find sanctuary.

Needless to say, the individual screens on the top should be tight-fitting and capable of being fastened securely against the onslaught of the winter winds and the neighbor's children. The side boards should be given a good coat of exterior primer paint on all surfaces and, after drying, a second coat of the best quality exterior house paint. Treated this way, the cage will last for many years without deteriorating.

After the boards have been painted and are dry, they can be nailed together to form the large box, right on the ground where they are to be established. Make sure that the ground is level and that the side boards fit tightly against the surface. It would even be an excellent idea to dig out a shallow trench, about two inches deep, and set in the frame, filling up around the sides after assembly. A stake made of one-by-four-inch lumber, pointed at one end, can be driven into the ground to a depth of a foot or so, tightly up against the outer sides of the frame—two to each side. The frame can then be nailed or screwed to these stakes and they will serve to secure the cage to the ground so wind, animals, or children will not shift it. Dividers can be fastened to slide down along the grid to divide the inner area into four small parts if you are interested in rearing more than one species of hibernating caterpillar simultaneously. This seriously depletes the number of sanctuaries the larvae will have, though, and should not be practiced unless you simply must rear more than one species at the same time. If you can recognize your animals, and tell one from the other when they are together, then it would be far better to just toss them all together and let them mix at will. Certainly there is no problem of mixing the species until the adults emerge, by which time you may have gathered all the cocoons and sorted them.

The young caterpillars can be introduced to their large home as soon as they have hatched. By that time the cage should have been seasoned for one year and the plants established within, and the tiny caterpillars can simply be transferred to their foodplant with a camel's hair brush. When you set up the cage for establishment, make sure there are no other insects left in the area, that the plants introduced are clean of any predators, and that the cage is kept closed all the time. In this manner you can be reasonably sure that the interior of the home is safe for your small animals.

A day after you have put in your caterpillars, you will be lucky indeed if you can find one single caterpillar after diligently searching the entire cage. They will all have disappeared into thin air, apparently, and will remain so until they are nearly full-grown. In the case of the fat and fuzzy "woolly-bears"—*Isia isabella*—you may see them parading around in the early fall in search of a nice place to spend the winter. In the early spring, they will be abroad again, looking for succulent leaves upon which to finish their growth. The same may be true of *Arctia caja*, although these and most others of the family are not prone to wander as much as *isabella*.

One difficulty in bringing these species through maturation in captivity is the danger of starving them to death on the warm days during the winter. They walk about expending energy, and need a leaf or two to nibble on in order to replenish themselves. Also, it seems as though they just require some sort of exercise during the cold weather, because often they may be seen in motion during the winter season. If, in captivity, the caterpillars are reared indoors on cut food, the chances are that they will continue right on feeding and go into their usual pupal stage without a diapause. This is fine if you are rearing for adult specimens, but not good if your intention is to create or maintain a race. If the latter is your aim, you are almost required to set up some place such as that described above. Otherwise the moths will emerge out of period, mate, and lay eggs which will then hatch with no food supply available. For papered or expanded specimens for collections, it is not necessary to erect an outdoor hibernaculum, but merely rear the animals to maturation and paper them for stock.

In the wild the caterpillars do not seem to have the problem of survival on warm days. Perhaps they do not awaken sufficiently to start to wander, but merely remain in the deep comatose state natural to them during the hard weather.

In captivity, the very finest conditions arranged for larvae are, at best, artificial and a substitute to them. One generation or even a thousand generations cannot learn to cope. The adaptation of a species for survival in changing environment is a long and tedious proposition, and countless millions of individuals die for every one that makes a tiny step towards evolution.

Another genus which may give the beginner some difficulty in rearing is *Automeris*. Not that they require any special attention—although certain species like certain conditions, none of them are really out of the ordinary in the full area of rearing moths. Where the *Automeris* moths are apt to give trouble is in the duration of the larval stage. The eggs hatch in early May, and the caterpillars will still be feeding in October, and even into the first week of November! Naturally, the food is not going to be at its best by then, if, indeed, there are any leaves at all left on the foodplants. One must resort to emergency measures in order to bring the caterpillars through to pupation.

First, when eggs of *Automeris* are obtained, they can be kept warm in order to hasten their hatching a few days. A tiny bit of cotton, saturated with water and placed in a closed zipper box with the eggs, but not touching the eggs themselves, will work wonders in shortening the hatching time. I have had eggs hatch a full four or five days before they normally could be expected, by keeping them a few degrees warmer than usual and keeping the cotton wet. This will give you an advantage at the beginning. The caterpillars should then be placed outdoors in order to build up their vigor and get some growth on them. About the middle of June—if the year has been a normal one in the respect of seasonal rainfall—you should start watering the plant the caterpillars are feeding upon daily, seeing that it is well saturated, and that the leaves themselves are given a light spray as well. This watering is to keep the leaves succulent through the drought period of summer.

Toward the end of August, say the beginning of the third week, you should test the leaves daily to make sure they remain succulent and fresh. By the end of August, or a bit earlier if the season is very hot and dry, you should start to gather food for storage, and bring the brood inside, feeding on cut food in water.

The storage of leaves will insure you a food source of good stock after the leaves on the growing plant have started to "leather" up.

In order to keep leaves usable, they should be thoroughly washed and shaken dry. Then small portions—enough for one renewal in the brooder—are packed tightly in a plastic bag, all the air possible expelled and the bag tightly shut. These bags may then be packed into a refrigerator and kept at an even temperature of between forty and forty-five degrees. *They must not be frozen.* Leaves kept in this way will remain succulent and fresh for several weeks, and may mean the difference between losing your entire brood and success in rearing them. When the brood in question is one of the particularly rare and desirable moths, it is well worth the effort and time to carefully prepare the leaves for storage. If you have no room in the family refrigerator, or if the mistress of the household takes objection to your using it for that purpose, the next best thing is to try to buy an old one somewhere. Usually a large box that is perfect for the purpose can be had for twenty-five dollars or less. (A good place to try for such an item is an apartment house superintendent.) Enough leaves can be stored in an old eight-foot box to last two or three broods through the fall weather, and the box can also be used to store overwintering stock such as eggs, pupae, cocoons, and possibly even hibernating larvae, as mentioned earlier in this chapter.

A method of keeping caterpillars over the winter that might work is one that I once used for hibernating reptiles. Snakes or lizards may be dropped into a clean well-sewn muslin drawstring bag, the top tightly tied shut, and the bag placed on a shelf in the refrigerator where the occupant will comfortably sleep through the entire winter season. In the spring, when food is again available, the animal is brought out, allowed to warm up gradually, and presto! It is alive and frisky—and hungry too!

A similar method might work in storing caterpillars, and, while I have not attempted to do so up until now, this year the woolly bears are so plentiful, I have set a brood inside to see how they will weather the year. A second brood is also in my outdoor hibernaculum as a control. Since caterpillars are much more susceptible to squashing than are reptiles, which also can be artificially hibernated in refrigerators, the larvae were placed inside a small plastic box instead of a muslin bag. A piece of window screening was bent to make a floor, or platform, about one-half inch above the bottom of the box so that any condensation which might occur would run down under the screen and the larvae would not drown. I do not know that condensation will form, but this precaution was no trouble and certainly will act as a safeguard. Incidentally, I might mention that the caterpillars were not taken from the road while they were wandering about looking for a spot of refuge, then refrigerated. They were first placed in the outdoor hibernaculum until the really cold weather set in and they were quite dormant. At that time a number were brought into refrigeration, and the remainder left in the hibernaculum as a control batch. If you have no all-winter cage, the same result may be obtained by putting some larvae in a small cage outside, feeding them constantly until they stop eating of their own accord and curl up for the winter.

If the larvae are put into cold storage before they are dormant, there is the possibility they might starve, not having been ready to go down for the winter. Of course, much study is needed before we can be sure of the best way of over-wintering hibernating larvae.

In connection with the use of refrigerated leaves, this might be a good place to mention artificial aids to nutrition of caterpillars. Many experiments have been made in this area, with varying amounts of success. Perhaps the best one was the development of Smith's Elixer. This is a solution made by Mr. W. R. Smith of Southampton, England, who was searching for the answer to two problems: a suitable mixture of ingredients, and a suitable method for getting the mixture into the caterpillar. Mr. Smith decided on the following "elixer" after a series of nutritional experiments.

Dextrose	2 tablespoons
Potassium Nitrate	1½ teaspoons
Brewer's Yeast	2 tablets
Water	1 pint

All the ingredients can be found in any good drugstore, and the mixture is very easy to make and use. Three methods are used to get the elixer on the foodplants. The branches of the plant can be stood in a bottle of the solution for at least twenty-four hours before being offered to the caterpillars; the undersides of the leaves can be painted with the solution and allowed to dry before using as food; or, the leaves can be sprayed with the solution from a clean flit-gun. While Mr. Smith, in his published account of the use of the solution, was careful not to make any claims of its value, but offered it as an experimental material, spectacular results have occurred with its use, and it is well worth further experimentation.

Many other experiments have been made with regard to rearing, triggering stubborn emergences, etc. In the latter case, it might be good to put down some notes which were sent to me by Mr. Otto Ackermann of Irwin, Pennsylvania, that were in turn sent to him by a well-known lepidopterist in Germany, Mr. J. Bijok. The notes have to do with the use of ultraviolet irradiation of pupae in order to trigger emergence. The light was used (in this experiment) on *Citheronia regalis* which had been shipped to Germany from the United States. The pupae (fifteen in number) were irradiated daily for twenty seconds, with an ultraviolet lamp held one meter (thirty-nine inches) away. Mr. Bijok reported that all the pupae emerged simultaneously, and that apparently the use of ultraviolet light synchronizes the final development of the insect within the pupa and triggers their emergence. The adults, which were placed in a screened cage, were subsequently irradiated with infrared light for a short time. The moths became very active, the three pairs copulated the first night after the irradiation, with approximately eighty percent hatching from the eggs.

Mr. Ackermann went on to say that Mr. Bijok had told him he had used this method of triggering for several years on many different species, always with excellent results.

Several lamps are available at moderate cost for persons who might wish to experiment in this area. The photographic lamp—Sylvania Sun Gun—is one quartz lamp which might give off enough ultraviolet to be useful. Or you might use any of the mineralights that are offered to collectors and students and that are available as a source of either long- or short-wave ultraviolet light (in different lamps). These lamps can be a danger to the user, in that he or she can seriously damage his eyesight by looking directly at the source of illumination. The user should never turn the lamp on when it is pointed at his eyes, and it is best to wear protective goggles or dark glasses.

Infrared lamps are obtainable at almost any hardware or electrical store. They are the familiar "heat lamps" and have a deep red glass. They are rated at 250 watts and give off an intense heat, so be careful not to cook your caterpillars—or yourself! Experimentation must be made with both these procedures, and accurate notes should be kept on the results, before we can definitely state the value or lack of value of irradiation. My personal experience is that *Citheronia regalis* is difficult to get to mate, and I have had the same complaint from many of my breeder friends, and anything that would trigger this act would be of inestimable value to the serious breeder.

The reason for breeding moths can be very different for different people. As stated earlier, many will want to breed commercially; some to obtain perfect specimens for their collections and those of their friends; and still others will engage in the task of rearing in order to photograph the life histories, or perhaps just the adults, of as many species as they can obtain.

Photographic and Mounting Equipment

It is not my intention to give the reader a course in insect photography in this volume. Such a chapter would be outside the area covered. However, a few hints as to equipment and the methods I used to photograph the specimens illustrated would not be amiss.

A single lens reflex-type of camera is almost a must when you are working with specimens that cannot be held still, such as caterpillars. With such a camera the photographer can follow the subject around and shoot when it is in a good position. I have found the Honeywell Pentax camera ideally suited for this exacting work, and use several of them as studio as well as field equipment. A special lens for use on the Pentax bellows makes the photographing of tiny eggs much easier than it would be using close-up attachments on your regular lens. Honeywell makes a ring light that can be operated on a.c. or can be powered for use in the field by any of several of their portable electronic-flash strobonars, making field photography of small caterpillars or eggs an easy task.

When photographing for identification or for presentation of a species as in this volume, for instance, all extraneous material should be excluded from the background. This makes the subject stand out so the observer can see discriminating features without the distraction of branches, leaves, other insects, etc. It is a simple matter to get this reduced background, by using a lens tube to enlarge the image of the specimen on the view finder and placing the subject in such a manner that nothing behind it is closer than four or five feet. If you are using black and white film, all that will show in the background is a series of varying shades of gray. If color film is used, the background will generally show up black, which is ideal for such work.

Eggs, in order to afford enough contrast from the background, can be placed on black construction paper if they are light in color, or on pale blue or pale green paper if they are dark in color.

If your purpose of rearing is to obtain perfect specimens for collections, then you must either learn to mount your adults or find someone who will perform the service for you.

The act of preparing a moth or butterfly for a mount is generally called "spreading." In Europe they say "setting." The task is not really a difficult one, but it goes without saying that it is very delicate. Scales are not firmly fastened to the fragile wings of the adult insects, and in the case of moths even less so than with butterflies. Butterflies generally have thinner wings and the scales are more tightly compacted on them. The overlap is tighter and the entire coating of scales lies more snugly to the membrane of the wing. Many moths have scales more thread-like than those of butterflies, giving the wings the appearance of being covered with fur rather than with overlapping plates. These delicate scales rub off with practically no abrasion at all, and a beginner who is learning to spread moths is apt to ruin many specimens before he achieves the knack of handling them.

The three areas of danger for the beginner in spreading specimens are: rubbing the scales off the wings, breaking the wings off the bodies, and pulling chips out of the wings.

Generally the reason for wings breaking off the bodies is that the specimen was not sufficiently relaxed in order to be spread. If you mount your specimens as soon as they have emerged from the cocoon and dried their wings, this difficulty will be eliminated since, for a matter of from several minutes to an hour or more, the insect will remain limp and flexible after it is killed. If, on the other hand, you paper your insects and store them for varying periods of time, as in the case of most rearers and collectors, the insect will dry out in the paper and become stiff, rigid, and very fragile.

Before such a specimen is spread, it must be returned to the state of relaxation where all the muscles are again flexible and the various members are easy to move. The whole of the insect is so fragile that even in the state of partial rigor mortis it cannot be handled without some damage occurring to the wings, antennae, or body. There are several ways to relax such dried specimens. Perhaps the most commonly used one is a damp box, or relaxing box as it is generally called.

A relaxing box is simply a container large enough to hold the insects you wish to relax, and to keep them suspended above a layer of wet absorbent material of some kind until the damp air within the box penetrates all the muscles of the subjects. An inch-thick layer of sand on the bottom of the box with a sheet of window screening held above it will serve admirably to relax your specimens. The sand should be wetted down thoroughly with warm water, to which a few drops of C-N, formaldehyde, formalin, or any of many disinfectants is added. The purpose of the addition is to discourage the formation of mold on the bodies or wings of the insect as it remains in the damp air. The papered insects are laid on the screen above the sand and the box tightly closed. It will take from several hours to several days to completely relax the insects, depending upon the size of the insects, the size of the box, and the amount of moisture in the sand.

A more permanent relaxing box can be made by pouring a thick layer of mixed plaster of paris into the bottom of a tightly closing metal box. This plaster can be saturated each time the box is used and the papered specimens placed on the surface of the plaster. However, it is better to make a screen trivet to put between the papers and the plaster, in case the disinfectant you use is oily, as is C-N. The oil might saturate the paper and ruin the specimen within. The bodies of many moths are oily enough as it is, and sometimes tend to bleed the oil all over the wings, thus ruining an otherwise perfect specimen.

A method of relaxing is practiced in Europe that is quite different from the relaxing boxes in general use in this country. When first I watched the European method I was certain that the specimens were ruined beyond reclaim. However, it works; and since then I have used this way of relaxing moths myself. The advantage is that the specimen is really thoroughly relaxed, even very large ones like the enormous Atlas moths. A frame is required, which can easily be put together by anyone, even though he is not a craftsman. Start with an old terry-cloth towel, folded in half. Assume that the folded towel measures twelve inches by eighteen inches. Using this as a basic measure we can assemble the relaxing frame as follows:

Parts needed: one piece of plywood, not thinner than one-half inch, and measuring twenty-one and one-half inches by fifteen and one-half inches. Stock one-by-two-inch lumber—obtainable from any lumber company—sufficient to cut into two pieces *each*, twelve and one-quarter inches long, and twenty-one and one-half inches long. Nail these pieces to the surface of the plywood, the longer ones flush with the long edges of the plywood, and the two shorter pieces flush with the short ends of the plywood. The strips should be nailed on a flat side, not stood on edge. The result will be a board with a fixed flat frame about three-quarters-inch deep all around it. A sheet of glass should be cut to drop into the bottom of this frame, and a second piece of glass cut to rest as a cover over the top of the frame.

To use: thoroughly wet the towel and wring it out just enough that it does not drip, but so that it is still quite wet. Spread one half of the towel in the frame to cover the glass in the bottom. The remainder of the towel will remain outside the frame. Sprinkle several drops of thymol alcohol on the towel and cover the wet towel with a single layer of paper toweling.

Lay all the specimens you are going to relax on the paper towel, seeing that they do not overlap one another. The specimens can be left in their papers or removed and put on the frame with no protection, as you desire. Cover the layer of specimens with a second layer of paper toweling, then carefully bring the remaining fold of the wet towel over the top of all, taking care that it lies smoothly on top of the paper and specimens and within the frame. Sprinkle several more drops of thymol alcohol on the top section of the wet towel and cover the entire affair with the larger sheet of glass. One half hour will be enough time to relax small specimens, three or four hours for large ones, and overnight for giant Atlas moths and similar specimens. The wings and bodies sometimes actually get wet with this method, but I have never ruined a specimen. They seem to dry out on the spreading board perfectly, and the colors are not changed or altered in any way. Certainly the insects are subject to thorough wetting when they are alive, with no apparent damage, and I suppose this wetting doesn't injure them any more than rain would.

The purpose of the addition of the thymol alcohol is to inhibit the formation of mildew on the wet bodies. Thymol alcohol can be mixed by yourself, or your local drugstore will make it for you. Simply dissolve one ounce of thymol crystals in a quart of ordinary rubbing alcohol. The resultant fluid will last for a long time, since you use only a sprinkle each time you relax a tray of specimens.

Mr. Max Richter, who is the owner of The Butterfly Farm in East Durham, New York, is one of the best preparators I have ever known. Elsewhere in this volume I have given you a picture sequence showing Mr. Richter in a step-by-step process of spreading a moth. In this text I will give you the detailed method.

Spreading boards of various sizes are needed in order to prepare specimens for mounting. These boards can be cheaply purchased from any biological supply house, or they can be made out of model airplane balsa wood. The purchased boards last for years, and it really is not worthwhile making your own unless you need a great many of them, or need some special size that is not obtainable in the store.

European preparators usually cover their boards with lined tablet paper before use. This provides a guide for lining up the wings, and at the same time provides a smooth surface on which to move the wings. In Europe, also, the claim is that a lion's whisker is the ideal spreading needle, because the whisker of a lion is stiff, yet flexible, curved just right for handling, and sharp enough to hook the wing without tearing it. In America we do not have a large source of lion's whiskers for this purpose. Certainly I know of no store that sells them, and, unless you want to walk up to a lion and yank a whisker out of its upper lip, you had better use a plain needle which you can make.

This can be easily fashioned out of a large thin needle, held over the burner of the kitchen range until it is red hot at a point about a half-inch from the tip; the tip should then be bent to a right angle to the shank and quenched in cold water to restore the temper; finally, polish the tarnish off with a piece of fine crocus or emery cloth. The needle may now be forced into the end of a short length of quarter-inch wooden dowel handle, and presto! you have a synthetic lion's whisker that will outlast any whisker you can obtain from the King of Beasts.

You should make up two of these needles, and two straight ones stuck in dowel handles the same way as the bent ones. A needle-pointed tweezer with a very soft action is also valuable. It must be very easy to close; if you cannot find any but stiff ones, they can be altered to suit your purpose by filing part way through each blade up near the closed end to thin down and weaken the spring. The tweezers should be limp enough to close without any pressure to speak of. If you have to squeeze hard to close the tweezer, it becomes almost an impossibility to regulate the amount of pressure so that you will grip the insect without punching through it with the tips of the tool.

A heavy, blunt, serrated-tip tweezer is needed to handle the pins both in fastening the insect down to the spreading board and in mounting specimens in the cases. These are called pinning forceps, and can be bought from biological supply houses. A pair of heavy dental forceps can also be used.

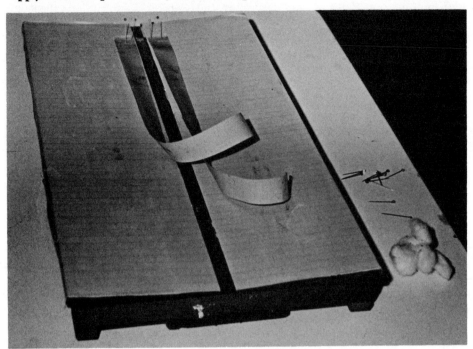

Mounting a Specimen Paper or tracing cloth strips should be fastened to the board on each side of the body groove

The spreading board is prepared for receiving the specimens by attaching two strips of paper at the sides of the groove. The strips are pinned to the board at one end, the other end left free until you start to spread. Draftsman's tracing cloth is probably the very best material available for this purpose: it is stiff, strong and has a glazed surface that will allow the wings to be pushed around under it without the nap of the cloth rubbing off the scales. A sheet of tracing cloth can be purchased for a few cents and will provide a good supply of strips three-quarters to one inch wide, and as long as the board.

After the specimen is relaxed to the point where it is really limp, and the wings move easily if you just puff between them, you are ready to start the spreading operation. First grasp the insect body firmly between a thumb and forefinger. Hold it so that it will not move, but not so tightly that you collapse the body. Select a pin with a shank diameter suited to the size of the body of the specimen you are working on, and hold it in the heavy forceps about midway on the shank.

Force the pin straight down through the thorax, holding the forceps between the wings from the hindwings forward. If you blow on the wings as you work, the wind will separate them enough for you to get your hand between without scraping the scales. Also, a slight pinching pressure of the fingertips holding the

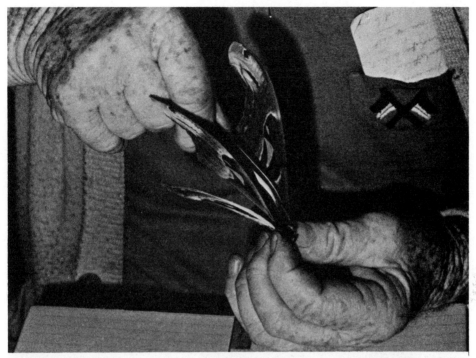

Mounting a Specimen The body is firmly grasped between the thumb and forefinger, and the pin, held in rigid tweezers, is pushed vertically through the thorax

specimen will help pull the wings apart. When the pin has penetrated the thorax, it should slide down about a half inch between your finger tips.

Without releasing your grip on the forceps holding the pin, carry the specimen over the spreading board and position the body in the center of the groove. A small amount of fluffy cotton in the groove under the point where you pin the insect will form a resilient support for the body without damaging it. Push the point of the pin into the board in the bottom of the groove until the body of the insect lies well within the groove. The wings should come just to the surface of the board. Now, with one of your bent needles, push the wings down together on one side of the insect, until they lie flat on the board. Pull the strip of tracing cloth over the wings and stretch it firmly until it hugs the surface of the board, then fasten it in place with a pin or two at the loose end. Perform the same operation on the other side of the insect.

Now, with the bent needle, stick the forewing close to the body and close up to the heavy costa or ridge at the leading edge of the wing. Do not puncture the costa. Push the wing forward until the rear edge is exactly perpendicular to the side of the body. If the body turns in the groove of the board, release the wing, realign the body, and put a couple of pins into the groove alongside the body to hold it firmly in place. Return the hook to the wing and push it up perpendicular to the body; then hold the wing in place by pushing a pin through the strip right up against the costa, but take care not to put the pin through the wing. A second pin through the tape will help hold the wing firmly. Position the bottom wing the

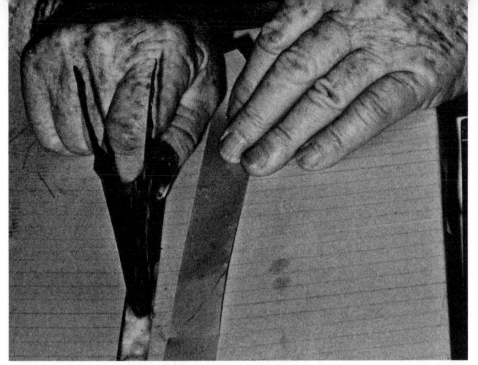

Mounting a Specimen The specimen, still held by the pin in the tweezer, is accurately placed in the groove of the spreading board. Push the pin down until the wing joints are just at the surface of the board

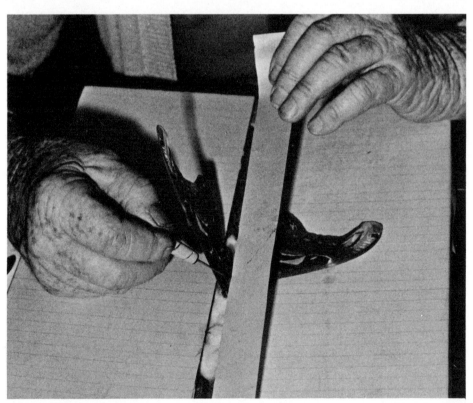

Mounting a Specimen With the setting needle, press one wing down and pull the strip over it to hold it flat

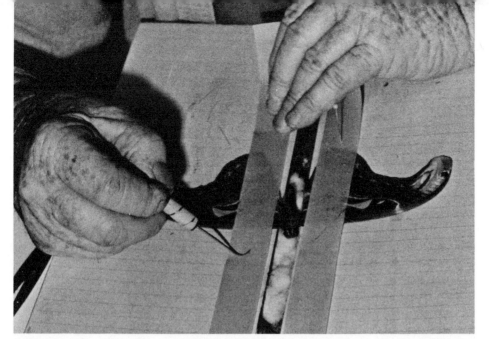

Mounting a Specimen The second wing is now brought down to the surface of the board and held in place with the strip. A pin is stuck through each strip to keep it in place

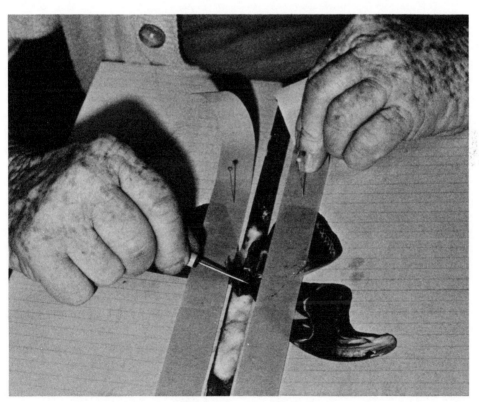

Mounting a Specimen The forewing is pushed up until the rear edge is exactly perpendicular to the body. The setting needle is used close to the costa and the body

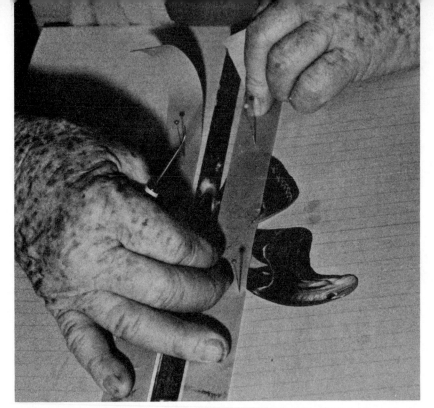

Mounting a Specimen Two pins are put through the strip as close to the costa as possible to keep pressure on the wing so that it does not slip back

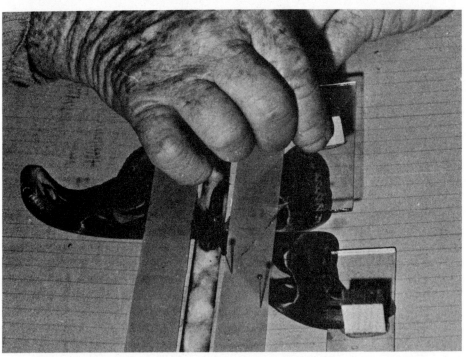

Mounting a Specimen A small strip of glass is now dropped onto the wing tips to keep them in place, and to keep from curling as the insect dries on the board

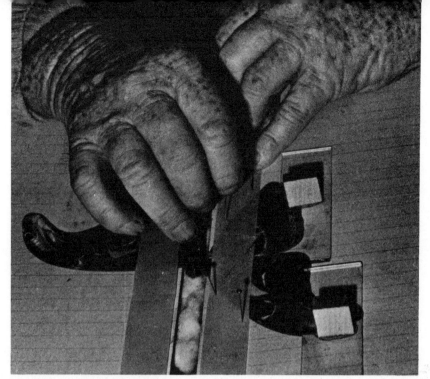

Mounting a Specimen Pins are now set through the strip at the hindwings to hold them firmly in place

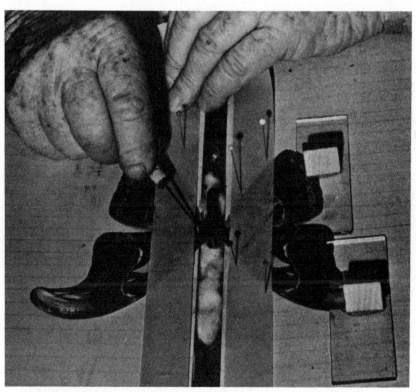

Mounting a Specimen The second side is set in position as before

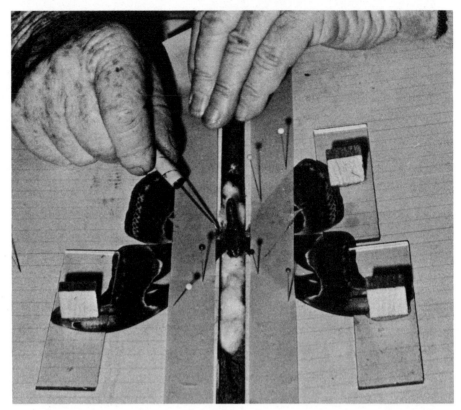

Mounting a Specimen In setting the hindwings, be very gentle, because they do not have the stiff costa to keep them from tearing. Stay very close to the body and to the front edge of the wing

same way, but be easier on this one because there is no firm stiff costa to keep the setting needle from tearing through the edge of the wing. As soon as one pair of wings is positioned, drop a small wafer of glass over the tips to hold them in place. If you glue a bit of balsa wood to the centers of the glasses, they will be more convenient to handle. Pins may now be pushed through the tape behind the hindwings to hold all firmly in place.

Position the wings on the second side of the insect. Be certain that the first wing is exactly perpendicular to the body, and that the second wing is exactly in a straight line with the first wing. If you use a papered board, the guide lines will help you. Otherwise, have a critical eye and be patient, and do not object to removing the pins and starting over again in order to get it right.

Drop the holding glasses into place as you progress, and when the final one is in place, pause and check carefully to see that all is in proper order. The amount that the hindwings should be pushed up under the forewings depends on their shape and the pattern of markings on both wings. You will find that generally the pattern falls into an obviously correct position when the center of the leading edge of the hindwing is just about in the outer third of the trailing of the forewing. The outer edges of the two wings should form a continuous sweep,

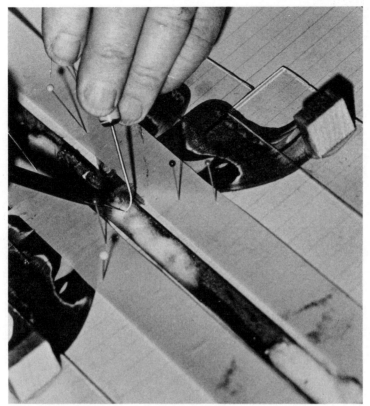

Mounting a Specimen After the wings are set and the pins and glasses in place, cotton is pulled up to the head of the insect to support the antennae

broken only by the notch of space between the fore and the hindwings. If the hindwings are pushed up too far, the finished specimen seems all squashed up, and if they are not pushed forward far enough, they droop and the finished specimen is very unsightly.

After the wings are set to your satisfaction, the glasses in place and the strips pinned securely, some loose cotton can be pulled up against the head of the insect to form a support for the antennae. These are now teased into position with two needles, and the pectination combed if it is disarranged. The antennae may then be pulled out into position over the edge of the board and a small glass weight dropped over them to hold them flat and secure while they harden up again.

The finished board is set aside for several days to allow the insect to dry out thoroughly. During this period it is necessary to protect it from other insects (e.g. spiders) that would damage the specimen, and from dust and dirt falling upon the wings. Dust is very difficult to get off once it covers a wing. Also, protection must be taken to keep objects from falling on the board and to prevent the board itself from slipping or falling. Inside an empty drawer is an excellent space to store the board for the drying period, unless you have a drying cabinet.

Specimens are best kept on pins in cases. Sometimes individual moths or groups

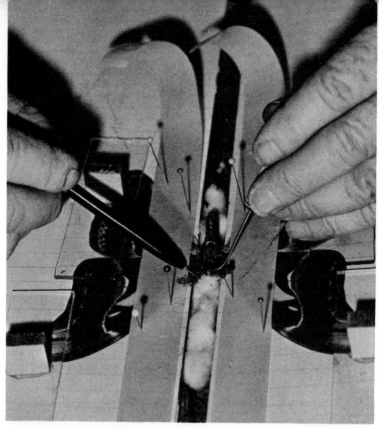

Mounting a Specimen The antennae are teased into an approximate position with two setting needles

of moths are placed in cotton-filled, glass-covered boxes called Riker Mounts. These mounts are not practical in that they ruin a specimen from a biological point of view. From the aesthetic viewpoint, Riker mounts are fine. A few exceptionally beautiful specimens can be put in them and the mounts hung on room walls as pictures. However, this is not the purpose for which a collection is usually made. A real collection of insects is an object of study. A series, for instance, of all the possible aberrations obtainable in the coloration of the wings of a certain species or a collection of hybrid varieties of a race of moths. There are any number of reasons for a study collection, but it must be preserved according to the best rules of natural history in order to be of value to its owner and to others. Attention should be paid to correct taxonomy. Poorly spread specimens, broken and rubbed wings, haphazardly arranged or incorrectly labelled collections are not acceptable: they are useless from a scientific point of view and, aesthetically, they offend the beholder.

The best cases are wooden boxes having an airtight seal and a glass top. They are available in several sizes, the most useful ones being approximately sixteen by twenty inches and three inches deep. Many companies make cabinet cases wherein each case is a drawer in a cabinet, and cabinets may be had to hold varying numbers of individual drawers. Most scientific supply houses carry them; however, some of these are very expensive. Of course, if you are handy with tools and have a place to work, excellent cases may be made yourself, and the cost thus cut drastically. The main idea is that each case must be airtight. There can be no ill-fitted joints, since spiders, other insects, dampness, and mold will all enter the

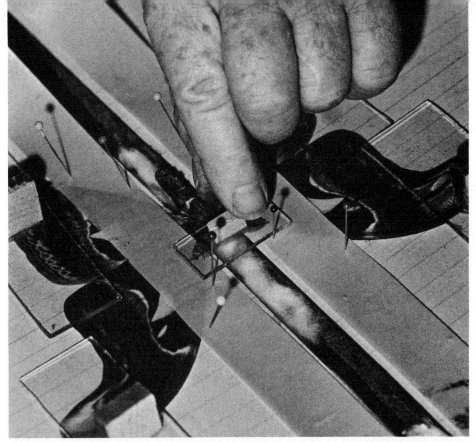

Mounting a Specimen The antennae can be flattened in place with a short glass, after they have been pulled into position and combed out with the setting needles. The completed specimen is now ready to dry for several days before removal from the board

tiniest crack. The bottoms of the cases can be made of one of the rigid plastic foams, or sheets of half-inch-thick Celotex. This last makes an ideal pinning bottom.

The spread and dried insects are impaled on insect pins. These are special, long, thin, stiff pins made for the purpose of mounting specimens. They come in several different thicknesses but uniform lengths. The thickness suited to each specific body size is selected and the pin is put through the body in the center of the thorax. About a quarter-inch of pin should be left standing out of the top of the specimen. This should be the same in all the specimens mounted in any case, so that the whole group are at the same level. Insect pins come in black japanned steel and in stainless steel. The black japanned ones are the best for permanent mounting for a number of reasons, the most important reason being that the heads are part of the shank and do not come off. It is extremely painful and a danger of infection to have the head slide down the shank of a pin, the shank penetrating your finger in the process, as you pin a specimen in the case. Also, the japanned pins, being rougher than the smooth stainless ones, grip the insect more firmly so the body does not swivel around on the pin after mounting in the case. If, after spreading and mounting, you find that the insect is loose on the pin, it can be removed from the case, the pin positioned, and affixed firmly to the body with the application of a drop of insect glue on the underneath side. Apply the glue to surround the shank of the pin, and make sure it is adhering to the body

31

Mounting a Specimen The finished specimen may be put in a safe place to dry, before removing it from the spreading board

and not just resting on top of loose body scales. You can "puddle" the glue with a pin or a toothpick to work it down through the body scales until it adheres to the shell of the body itself. After the glue is dry, the specimen can be returned to its location in the case.

Each specimen should be located in such a manner that there is room underneath it for a label. Labels should be small and stiff, and fixed to the bottom of the case with thin, short pins. Every label should carry the important data about the specimen: date taken, whether it was bred or wild caught, the location taken, and, if possible, the name of the collector. If specimens are bred, the usual designation is the use of "Ex," e.g., Ex-ovum, Ex-larva, Ex-pupa, depending upon whether you started with the egg, the caterpillar, or the cocoon. This is simple and clear, it being self-evident that if the designation is Ex-ovum the observer realizes at once that the specimen was obtained as an egg, hatched, reared to the diapause and then emerged. All this information is packed into one short word!

Specimen labels can be obtained from school and scientific supply houses in many different sizes. They come in sheets printed on fine card stock. The indi-

Mounted Specimens A well-filled mount of *Sphingid* moths. In this arrangement they look like bomber planes

vidual labels can be written if you can write a fine legible hand, or typewritten, then cut apart and fastened under the mount.

A well-arranged mount, with the specimens all perfectly spread and correctly labelled, is a thing of beauty and interest. Some sort of biological order should be maintained in mounting—species of one genus, or specimens of one family, such as all *Sphingid* moths, all *Saturnids,* etc. Or the mount might be a series of variations of one distinct species, such as a suite of *Arctia caja,* for instance, which has many variations in the coloration and markings of the hindwings as well as color variants such as melanism and albinism. Or specimens can be arranged in mounts according to location of range, i.e., all moths from New York State, or moths of Africa, or any other desired division of locality. Any way to keep your collection is acceptable, as long as a specific order is maintained throughout all the mounts.

If you use cabinets in which the mounts are drawers, it would be a help to label each drawer as to the contents. This way you would not have to start pulling drawers out one after another, stopping only when you came to the one you wanted to examine. A brass label holder could be fastened to the fronts of the drawers, if they were not so equipped on purchase, and enough data put on the label to identify the contents.

A small container of paradichlorobenzine or naptha flakes should be kept in the lower right-hand corner of each case. This is to keep spiders and other insects such as museum beetles out of the cases. The repellent should be renewed once or twice a year, as it evaporates slowly and will finally disappear entirely. In other words you have to be careful to "keep bugs out of your bugs," because a spider (some of which are so small as to be difficult to see without a strong magnifying glass) can cause havoc in a case in a very short while, especially because they eat the bodies of the mounted insects, allowing the wings to fall where they may. The fact that the bodies of the mounted specimens may contain cyanide from the killing jar and in turn kill the spider that ate it is no consolation to you for a ruined specimen. The damage once done can rarely be repaired.

Duke Downey of Sheridan, Wyoming, sorting cocoons preparatory to storing them in plastic containers for the winter

Winter storage of cocoons and pupae is a most important part of rearing moths. Unless the living creatures are properly attended to during their diapause, you will find yourself with no breeding stock in the spring.

Cocoons should be spread out on a table and carefully sorted over to pick out any that are dead or parasitized before putting them away for the winter. Dead cocoons may be identified by their lack of weight as compared with healthy living ones. Cocoons with a hole in them are almost certain to be parasitized, and these

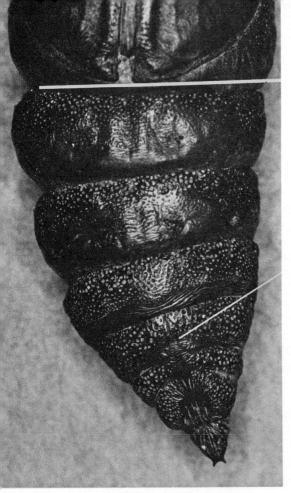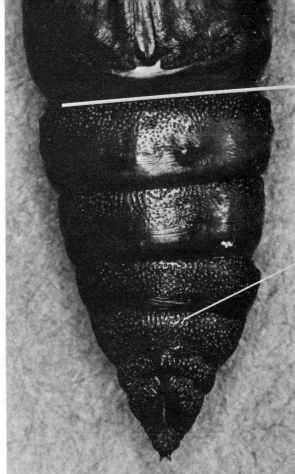

Identification of Sex in the Pupa If the fourth segment below the one covered by the bottoms of the wing cases is notched, lined, or broken in any way, the pupa is a female

Identification of Sex in the Pupa If the fourth segment below the one covered by the bottoms of the wing cases is intact, the pupa is always a male

should be discarded or at least separated from the others and stored alone to see what the parasite is when it emerges in the spring. Pupae should be left in the ground over the winter whenever and wherever feasible. When this is not possible, the pupae should be carefully dug up out of the ground or the pupating boxes, and put into soft paper tubes made by rolling a small square of paper towel around your finger and stapling one end shut. Slip the pupa into a tube, and then all may be stacked in cigar boxes or plastic containers accurately labelled. The boxes may be stored in a refrigerator at around forty degrees, or, if a protected area is available, they can be stored outdoors through the winter.

Pupae can be stored as separate sexes if desired, so you will know just what breeding stock you have of each species. Sexing naked pupae is very easy. Holding the pupa in a good light, count down the segments below the one covered by the ends of the wing cases. If the fourth segment below this one is marked, notched, split, or otherwise *not completely intact*—the pupa is a female. If the fourth segment below that covered by the tips of the wing cases is entire, then the pupa is male.

Sexing cocoons is more difficult. Many breeders make a practice of splitting open the cocoon with a razor blade just enough to open a small window to see the pupa within. The pupa is then sexed according to the method given above. Other breeders judge the sex by weight. Hefting a cocoon in one hand, those which seem heavier are deemed to be females, and the lighter ones, males. This method, quite surprisingly, is accurate most of the time. However, often you get dwarf females or giant males. These are exceptions and make for the misses in sexing by weight, but, especially in cocoons of *polyphemus, pernyi,* and similar large fat pupae, there is a noticeable difference in the weight of a male and a female, the latter being considerably heavier. There are certain species that will not survive to emerge if the cocoon is opened. Notable among these are the *Cerura* moths. If the fortress-like cocoon of this moth is split or otherwise broached, the pupa within is almost certain to die before emergence or to fail to survive the period of emergence.

Cocoons and pupae should be periodically sprayed with tepid water during the winter months. They should never be allowed to dry out completely. One sprinkling each week should suffice for pupae in paper sleeves, and the same for cocoons, provided they are stored in boxes where the moisture is not immediately evaporated from them. Fast evaporation chills the pupae too much, and should be avoided. On the other hand, if the pupae are stored in closed containers with little or no ventilation, mildew is apt to form, which can enter the spiracles of the pupae and kill them by suffocation. Leaving the tops just ajar after sprinkling is a good way to keep mildew from forming.

Fall is an excellent time of year to search for wild cocoons. Lunas, for instance, like to spin their cocoons up among the rubble and leaves at the foot of their food trees, and later to be covered with the blanket of fallen leaves from the same tree; the leaves afford visual concealment as well as protection from the freezing cold. Before the snow is on the ground, a careful sifting of such leaf falls is sure to yield a few good fat cocoons of wild stock to replenish your bloodlines.

Shrubby areas and patches of dense high reeds and weeds are good places to search for cocoons of polyphemus and cecropia. Look for them down near the ground and attached to the stems of the shrubs or reeds. Squat down and part the shrub so you can look right through it; then any cocoon is clearly delineated against the sky. Many wild cocoons will be parasitized but many will be healthy, and wild cocoons are always a welcome addition to a breeder, to avoid inbreeding of his comparatively small stock.

Another way to introduce new bloodlines is to use bred females, tying them out on a leash of thin thread fastened to a piece of screening and hung up on low branches of trees away from the house. The tethered females will broadcast their mating odors, attracting wild males who will mate with them. Of course, this method can only be used with species indigenous to your area. Some European breeders make a practice of liberating all the males of imported species, as soon as they emerge. Then, as females emerge, they leash them in the hope of attracting the males back to mate. To me, this seems a bit futile. There is the risk of losing your males, of course. There is also the violation of the prime unwritten law of a breeder which is not to liberate *any* species that is not indigenous, even though it be only one sex; and the whole idea defeats its purpose to begin with, since the males are not wild but from the same lot that you imported, so you have

Paul E. Stone, of Munith, Michigan, collecting cocoons of *Cecropia* and *Polyphemus*

no new bloodline, after all. The fact that the males are free does not mean they are wild.

When leashing out females, a cotton thread harness is tied around the thorax loosely enough to cause no constriction, but tightly enough to retain the insect. A crossed harness from in front of to behind the wings is best, since this can be left quite loose without danger of the moth escaping, since the wings will not easily slip through the loop. Leave a foot or so of thread on the leash, and tie the loose end to a piece of window screen. The moth will be able to find foothold on the screen and cling while the mating is in progress.

The screen, with the female attached, may be hung on a tree, a clothes pole, or any convenient support a bit away from the house. It should be hung out in the late afternoon and allowed to remain through the night. Some species (such as *Callosamia promethea*) fly in the afternoon, starting around four o'clock, so the females should be put out a bit earlier.

One danger in tying out is that of birds attacking the tethered moths. It is a simple matter for a hungry and alert bird to swoop down and neatly pluck the victim off the leash. One way to avoid this is to make the screen into a large cylinder, not less than a foot in diameter, and to tether the female moth on the inside of the cylinder. Make sure the leash is not so long that the moth will walk outside the screen. If the cylinder is large enough, the males can find their way inside with no difficulty in order to pair off. Birds will very seldom enter such an enclosure. They might alight upon the screen and peck at the moth from the outside, but generally—outside of frightening the unhappy captive—this causes no harm.

The mated female, after the two moths separate, can be dropped into a paper bag, folded over at the top and labelled. She will deposit her eggs on the inside of the sack, after which they can be cut out on little patches of the paper and stored for hatching.

The eggs should not be picked off the paper after they are laid, since the shells are so fragile that often the lower half will remain in contact with the support and the wet insides be smeared over your fingers. If you want to get eggs to photograph, the female should be placed in a box with a piece of the background material or paper on the bottom. She will obligingly lay some of her eggs on the bottom, and you may then remove the background for your picture taking.

Polyphemus moths mating on a twig. Any sturdy support which will allow the female to get a good foothold will do for most of the larger silk-moths

With some of the larger and more docile moths, mating is no problem at all, and can be undertaken indoors in cages or even out free in the room. A support must be offered to the female. *Polyphemus* will mate readily if the female is perched at the top of a stout twig where she can obtain a good foothold. In fact, most of the *Antheraea* will give you no trouble in mating in captivity. The silkworm moths generally mate before they have even expanded their wings fully and, in fact, it is not at all uncommon to find two males in copulation with the same female simultaneously, as the accompanying picture will testify.

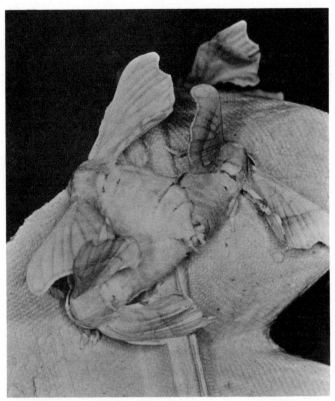

Bombyx mori It is not unusual to have two males in copulation with one female at the same time. The background is the egg box in which the larvae spun their cocoons

Matings vary considerably in duration. Some moths remain in copulation for only a few minutes. At the other extreme, pernyi will continue their coupling for twenty-four hours and even longer. Also, in the case of healthy stock, one male will service two, three, or even more females one after the other, with practically no rest period between.

Index of Life Histories

Amorpha populi Mounted adult female

Amorpha populi Pupa

Amorpha populi Fifth instar larva

AMORPHA POPULI

Family   Sphingidae

Popular Name   Poplar Hawk, in England

Range   Generally distributed throughout Europe and Great Britain

Availability   Usually available from European dealers, and generally offered by domestic breeders.

Preferred Foodplant   Poplar—as its specific name suggests

Accepted Alternate Foodplants   Willow, Birch, and Aspen

Diapause   Subterranean pupa

Ova   Medium large, oval. The shell is clear with a pearly nacrescence, the contents making the egg appear pale yellow. As the embryo forms within the shell, the egg turns pale green. After hatching, the empty shell is again clear.

Larvae   Pale green, as are almost all the *Sphingid* larvae. The anal horn is well pronounced. On attaining the later instars, the caterpillar becomes covered with tiny nodules and assumes a rough texture.

Rearing Requirements   Nothing special. The caterpillars are well able to withstand our climatic conditions. They do equally well cage-reared or outdoors. If reared in the warm south, they may make a second brood, but in the temperate zones of this country *populi* are single brooded. The newly hatched larvae eat part of their shells.

Cocoon   This moth does not require a deep pupating box, since the caterpillar digs just under the surface in order to make its pupa. Pupa is small and plump, with a rough surface texture.

Adult   The moth is very variable, as is the caterpillar, and is not conspicuously colored. Darkish gray base color with wavy black and light markings. The hindwings have a rust colored patch at the bottom edges. There is also a pink variation.

Calasymbolus myops Mounted adult female

Calasymbolus myops Fifth instar larva parasitized by Ichneumon or Braconid pupae. The victim is not aware that it is dead

Calasymbolus myops Pupa

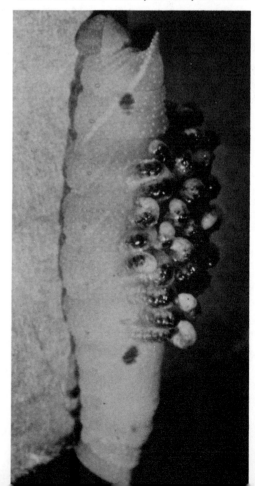

CALASYMBOLUS MYOPS

Family Sphingidae

Popular Name Small-Eyed Sphinx

Range Canada to Florida, and from the Eastern Seaboard to the Mississippi

Availability Almost always available from domestic breeders, or wild females may be attracted to lights and eggs obtained from them.

Preferred Foodplant Cherry

Accepted Alternate Foodplants Willow, several species of the Rosaceae, Privet, Lilac, and others

Diapause Subterranean pupa

Ova Like most of the eggs of the sphinx moths, these are small, oval, pale green with a slight depression on the sides.

Larvae Light green-yellow. Small—under two inches in length, some specimens have yellow diagonal lines margined with red on the lateral surfaces. Others lack the red, and the yellow lines are pale and indistinct.

Rearing Requirements Cannot stand too much crowding and prefer living food to cut branches, but will survive if reared indoors. The caterpillars do not go very far underground to pupate.

Cocoon Spun in a cavity under two or three inches of soil, the cocoon is flimsy and serves only to hold the dirt away from the pupating chamber. The pupa is medium size with straight sides tapering rather abruptly to the tail end. Dull surface and slightly rough to the touch. Strongly indented abdominal segments. The tail is short, but very sharp. Dull brown in color.

Adult Brown forewings with darker markings and black tracery. The outer edges are wavy in shape, with a pronounced indent in the trailing edge. The span is about two inches. The hindwings are dark yellow with light brown markings and a black ocellus with a white center midway on the wings. The body is brown with black defining lines at the abdominal segments. Antennae are short, stiff, and hooked at the ends.

Celerio euphorbiae Fifth instar larva. A real dandy of the caterpillar clan

Celerio euphorbiae Mounted adult female

CELERIO EUPHORBIAE

Family Sphingidae

Popular Name Spurge Hawk Moth

Range European Continent generally; sometimes a migrant to Great Britain

Availability Generally always available from European dealers, and often from breeders in the United States.

Preferred Foodplant Cypress Spurge (*Euphorbia cyparissias*)

Accepted Alternate Foodplants Sea Spurge (*Euphorbia paralias*)

Diapause Subterranean pupa

Ova Small, round, apple green, and shiny. After the caterpillar has hatched the shells are pearly and transparent.

Larvae The caterpillar of *euphorbiae* is probably the most colorful of all the Sphinx larvae. There are several color variations, often in the same brood, although the different color markings of the larvae do not seem to influence the adults, which are uniformly colored and patterned. The ground color of the body is black. A bright red stripe runs down the center of the dorsal surface, and a broken red stripe along each side just below the spiracles. The entire body is covered with rings of small yellowish-white dots, and at the beginning of each segment a large dot of the same color on a wide clear black area. The caterpillar is smooth, with the anal "horn" being the only adornment other than the gaudy coloration. Fairly thick and nubby on the outer end, the horn is black at the tip and red on the lower half.

Rearing Requirements The species will do well on growing plants of its natural food, but seems to languish and expire before the completion of its life cycle if fed on cut food or on species of spurge other than the two mentioned here. Cypress Spurge, which in Germany is called Wolf's Milch, grows easily and abundantly from starter roots. The caterpillars can be kept happy by surrounding a section of the spurge with a large low box, covered with a screen to prohibit the entrance of predators. The fully grown larvae attain a growth in excess of three inches, but their appetites are not to be compared with that of the "sausage" type of caterpillar such as *Antheraea*.

Cocoon *Euphorbiae* spins a thin silk cocoon just under the surface of the ground, and generally utilizes leaves and dirt in the fashioning of the walls. It may remain in the pupal stage for over a year, or it may emerge as the adult in two weeks. The pupa is light brown and slightly flattened at the tail end. The wing cases are marked with darker brown.

Adult The moth has a large body in comparison to its wing size. Green-brown at the thorax shading into deep tan or light brown on the abdominal segments with white stripes delineating the segments. The forewings are rose-tan ground with pale chestnut patches along the costa, which is greenish in color. There is an elongated triangle running the entire length of each forewing, of the same shade of chestnut as the patches. The hindwings are red with two black stripes and a white patch on the inner edge. This is an elegant moth, trim and neat in color and markings. The short stiff antennae are white. Wingspan about three inches.

Celerio lineata Mounted adult male

Celerio lineata Pupa

Celerio lineata The larvae come in several color phases. This is the second instar of the black phase

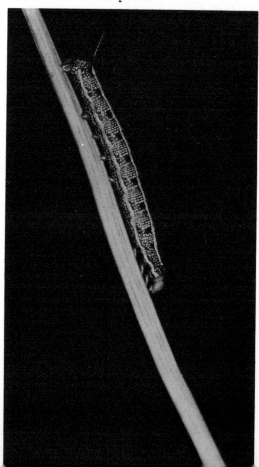

CELERIO LINEATA

Family   Sphingidae

Popular Name   Striped Hawkmoth—Striped Morning Hawk

Range   North America

Availability   Generally always available from larger breeders.

Preferred Foodplant   Purslane (*Portulaca*)

Accepted Alternate Foodplants   Virginia creeper and grape

Diapause   Pupa

Ova   Like most of the eggs of the *Sphingidae*. Oval, pale green, turning darker when ready to hatch.

Larvae   This caterpillar has many color phases and varieties, one of the most common being black with yellow spots scattered on the segments. There is a pink to yellow stripe down the dorsal line, and yellow lines along the sides. Spiracles are yellow. The body is smooth and hairless, and the horn is black.

Rearing Requirements   Nothing special for this species except to see that your cages or sleeves are tightly closed, since this caterpillar has a very small head, being thereby capable of escaping through quite small openings. Crowding is not recommended, and a clean and airy condition is best for healthy larvae.

Cocoon   *Lineata* spins a very flimsy silken cocoon just near the surface of the ground inside of which it pupates. The pupa is long and doubly tapered toward the ends. Roughly surfaced and somewhat dull in appearance.

Adult   This is a truly handsome moth, elegantly trim in coloring and design. A broad white stripe runs through the center of the forewings, from which thin short stripes branch off both sides, dividing the brown area of the wings into rectangular patches. The hindwings are a wonderful shade of pink with a black band coloring the front and rear edges. A striped cape of fur covers the thorax. Wingspan from three to four inches.

Ceratomia amyntor Pupae

Ceratomia amyntor Fifth instar larva. The surface of these caterpillars is beautifully textured

PHOTO BY PAUL E. STONE, MUNITH, MICHIGAN

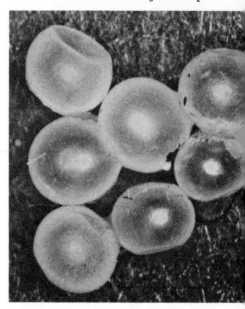

Ceratomia amyntor Ova

Ceratomia amyntor Mounted adult female

CERATOMIA AMYNTOR

Family   Sphingidae

Popular Name   Four-Horned Sphinx

Range   From Canada to the Carolinas, and from the Eastern Seaboard to the Mississippi Valley

Availability   Eggs or pupae may generally be obtained from one American breeder or another. They are often available from European breeders who have obtained stock from the United States and have maintained races in their countries.

Preferred Foodplant   Elm

Accepted Alternate Foodplants   None to my knowledge

Diapause   Pupa

Ova   Like most of the ova of the *Sphingidae* these are small, oval, and pale green; the shells are transparent and pearly after hatching.

Larvae   In the last instar this is a very beautiful and unusual caterpillar. The entire body is covered with a rough skin, with a row of raised protuberances along the dorsal line; a similar line runs diagonally in front of each spiracle almost to the dorsal line. The second and fourth segments each carry a pair of knobby horns and the *Sphingid* "tail" also is rough in texture. The whole effect is most striking. The colors vary, and the larvae have several color stages, the usual one being green with the only variation being the shadows cast by the rugose skin. There is a brown stage as well as a green stage mottled with brown.

Rearing Requirements   Rearing *amyntor* requires fresh elm leaves. They do not take well to cut food, although I have brought one brood to successful maturation indoors during an epidemic of predators. Elm does not retain its moisture content well and wilts rather rapidly, which is probably the reason these larvae prefer living trees to feed upon. They do not require moist humid conditions—rather they prefer light, airy locations.

Cocoon   The larva does not go too deep underground, and in my experience seems to prefer to dig into light loamy soil. The cocoon is flimsy, not really being worthy of the name. The pupa is long and stout. Rough in surface texture; dark red-brown with deeply indented segments. The tail is long and sharp.

Adult   The general overall color is gray-brown with wavy markings covering the forewings. There is a white spot in the upper center of each forewing. The hindwings are plain gray with a dark band running across near the bottom edge. The body is long and stout, thickly covered with hairs. Three broken dark bands run the length of the body from the thorax to the end. The antennae are stiff and wiry with a hook at the end. Span three inches or more.

Darapsa myron Mounted adult male

Darapsa myron Pupa

Darapsa myron Fifth instar larva. The swelling at the front end is indicative of this species

DARAPSA MYRON

Family   Sphingidae

Popular Name   Hog Sphinx. (Probably due to the enlargement of the third and fourth segments resembling the jowls of a hog.)

Range   Eastern Seaboard as far west as Kansas and Iowa

Availability   Generally available from domestic dealers. Very much sought after by European breeders.

Preferred Foodplant   Grape, either wild or domestic

Accepted Alternate Foodplants   Virginia Creeper

Diapause   Subterranean pupa

Ova   Small, green-yellow, ovate with a slight depression on the sides.

Larvae   The caterpillar is short and stout with a granular surface texture. The dorsal surface is dark green with a yellow triangle pointing backwards from each segmental line. A round, dark red spot in the center of each triangle. The green on the back extends all around the thoracic segments. Otherwise the lower half of the body is blue, with a green diagonal strip running from in front of each spiracle. The spiracles are small and red. The thoracic segments are curiously swollen at the sides, giving an odd bulge to the front of the caterpillar.

Rearing Requirements   *Myron* will thrive on cut leaves as well as on living food. Since it is a small caterpillar, the cage need not be a large one to accommodate a brood of normal size. They do not like it stuffy and humid, but prefer airy conditions. They also like direct sunlight, although they will go underneath the leaf to find relief if the sun is too intense. The colors turn muddy when pupation time arrives. These caterpillars are very subject to parasitization by *Ichneumons* and *Microgasters*.

Cocoon   The caterpillar goes underground for a short distance, or it may spin up on the surface just under debris. The cocoon is very flimsy, just a few threads of silk, and the pupa within is in full view. The pupa is tan with dark brown spiracles, and lines marking the segments. The wing cases are well defined.

Adult   A very trim, small moth. The forewings are tannish-gray with two broad darker bands crossing them and a small dark spot centered near the top. The hindwings are orange-tan shading to darker tan at the bottom edges. The antennae are short, stiff, and hooked. Body long and pointed, light gray with dark bands defining the abdominal segments. Span about two inches.

Deidamia inscriptum Mounted adult male

Deidamia inscriptum Third instar larva on wild grape

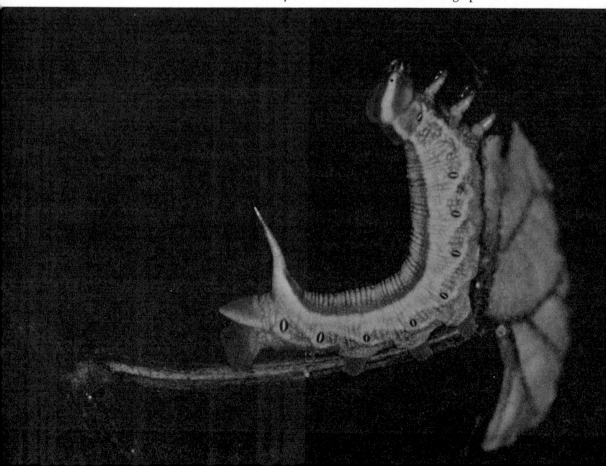

DEIDAMIA INSCRIPTUM

Family   Sphingidae

Popular Name   Lettered Sphinx

Range   Canada to Virginia and west to the Mississippi. However, this moth seems to be rare over most of its habitat.

Availability   Not often available. The only stock I have been able to obtain was collected wild in the second and third instars, and from a gravid female collected at a lighted window.

Preferred Foodplant   Wild grape

Accepted Alternate Foodplants   Domesticated grape, Virginia Creeper

Diapause   Pupa

Ova   Quite small, yellow-green, translucent.

Larvae   Body yellow with fine ridges all over the skin. The dorsal area is bluish with a yellow stripe running the length of the back. Spiracles rimmed in black; "S" shaped stripes diagonally behind each spiracle.

Rearing Requirements   This is an easy moth to rear. It is my experience that every caterpillar that feeds upon grape will also accept Virginia Creeper, and this one is no exception. The larvae are fairly small—about one and one-half inches when fully grown, so the cage need not be a large one. They do like it cool and airy, though.

Cocoon   The larvae spin a makeshift cocoon just under the surface of the ground, or among the rubble on the surface. The pupa is short, fat, and deep chestnut in color. The tail is quite sharp.

Adult   A pretty little moth, but I cannot see where the name *inscriptum* comes in any more than the nickname of "lettered moth." The forewings are deep clear gray with irregular bands of black to deep brown crossing them. The outer edges are deeply indented and irregular. The hindwings are dull tan or light brown with an obscure darker band at the lower edge. The abdomen is very dark and sharply constricted toward the tail. A short brush of hairs adorns the extremity of the body. Wingspan about one and one-half inches.

Hyloicus gordius Mounted adult male

Hyloicus gordius Pupa

Hyloicus gordius Fourth instar larva

HYLOICUS GORDIUS

Family   Sphingidae

Popular Name   According to Mr. Holland, this moth is called the Gordian Sphinx

Range   The entire United States as far west as Colorado

Availability   One domestic breeder or another is sure to offer this species each season. Duke Downey in Sheridan, Wyoming, often offers eggs or pupae.

Preferred Foodplant   Rosaceae of various species

Accepted Alternate Foodplants   Dogwood (*Cornus*), Ozier, Crab Apple

Diapause   Subterranean pupa

Ova   The usual sphingid egg—smallish, oval, pale green with a slight depression on the sides.

Larvae   In the earlier instars, this caterpillar is ridiculously out of proportion, with a tail "horn" almost half as long as its body—stiff, sharp, and bright red. The body is green and completely covered with small protuberances, giving the animal a pebbled appearance. Seven diagonal white lines point rearward from in front of the small, orange spiracles; the last line runs up into the horn. Each white line has a deep violet line in front of it.

Rearing Requirements   Does not like crowding, and prefers an airy, coolish rearing condition. Prefers fresh food to cut leaves, although it will carry through to maturation indoors if the leaves are changed frequently and kept succulent. Also, this species seems to languish if the cage is not kept immaculately clean.

Cocoon   The pupa of *gordius* is long, stout, and deep chestnut in color. The wing cases are rough and dull, while the remainder of the surface is a bit more glossy and smooth. There is a very short proboscis case, not too well separated from the main body. The tip is very sharp and long.

Adult   The moth of this species does not differ radically from others in the same genus. The forewings are gray with a few cryptic black lines marking them. The hindwings are dark gray with a white band transversing them. The thorax is dark gray and the abdomen has three white bands. There is a light gray dorsal line decorated with a narrow black line in the center. Span about two and one-half inches or more.

Hyloicus kalmiae The proboscis case on the pupa is close to the body instead of curved outward like a jug handle

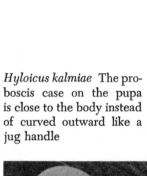

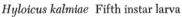

Hyloicus kalmiae Fifth instar larva

Hyloicus kalmiae Ova

Hyloicus kalmiae Mounted adult male

HYLOICUS KALMIAE

Family   Sphingidae

Popular Name   Laurel Sphinx

Range   Middle Atlantic States

Availability   Sometimes offered by domestic breeders, but more often obtained at collecting lights or lighted windows. Very popular in Europe.

Preferred Foodplant   Mountain Laurel (*Kalmia latifolia*)

Accepted Alternate Foodplants   Privet, Lilac, Fringe-Tree or Old Man's Beard—(*Chionanthus virginicus*)

Diapause   Subterranean pupa

Ova   The same as all the sphingid ova—smallish, oval, light green with transparent shells.

Larvae   A very elegant animal, in a dress suit. The body is green and there are seven diagonal white stripes on the sides, each stripe bordered in the front in black. The horn is pebbly and shiny black. The prolegs are yellow and black and the rear surface of the claspers are yellow peppered with tiny black spots.

Rearing Requirements   Maintain a low population density in the cages, and, if possible, rear them in a shady location rather than in bright sunshine. This is one of the species that is best reared outdoors in large sleeves or cages. They mature rapidly and are not subject to most diseases, but predators attack them readily. For this reason, a cage is to be preferred rather than a sleeve. The stripes on the sides darken just before time of pupation.

Cocoon   *Kalmiae* goes underground for a short distance and pupates within a cavity lined with a few strands of silk. The pupa is dark and smooth, slender and pointed. There is a short proboscis case but it is tight against the body case, not separated as in *Protoparce* pupae. The wing cases are very long, and the head end is curiously depressed laterally.

Adult   The wings are silvery gray, with somewhat indistinct markings of darker gray. The hindwings are marked with two bands of white, and the dark gray body has a broad light stripe lined with a narrow stripe of black down the back. There are four white bars on each side of the dorsal stripe, indicating the separation of the segments. Wingspan about three inches.

Hyloicus pinastri The striped larvae of this species are almost impossible to detect among the needles of their foodplants

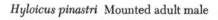

Hyloicus pinastri Mounted adult male

HYLOICUS PINASTRI

Family   Sphingidae

Popular Name   Pine Hawk

Range   Europe, Great Britain, and the United States. (Although fairly rare in this country, specimens have been taken in Pennsylvania.)

Availability   Generally available from European breeders.

Preferred Foodplant   Pine, as is suggested by the name

Accepted Alternate Foodplants   None to my knowledge

Diapause   Pupa, underground

Ova   Fairly small, oval, pale green.

Larvae   This is an interesting caterpillar, and one that shows a remarkable camouflage. It is pale yellow on hatching. In the next few instars the caterpillar is longitudinally striped in yellow and bright green, and when it lies along a branch of the pine tree upon which it is feeding it is virtually impossible to detect. In the final instar the body turns a dark chestnut or brownish red. Even then it is hard to detect as it lies along the main stem of the pine, which is very like the body color of the animal.

Rearing Requirements   It has been my experience that *pinastri* does not do too well indoors on cut food. This is also the case with a number of pine-feeding lepidoptera, which leads me to believe that pine is rather deceptive. Although it appears fresh and succulent, it really loses too much moisture to allow it to remain a good source of food. Perhaps, too, there are other chemical changes that take place in the material after it has been cut for a time that make it toxic or unable to support the larvae. When the caterpillars are ready to pupate, they become very active and run about. They do not go far underground, but pupate near the surface.

Cocoon   The pupa is somewhat narrow and small, glossy red-brown, darker between the segments. The proboscis sheath is rough and attached to the case. There is a shorter spike on either side of the tail spike.

Adult   The moth is somewhat somber—in common with most of the genus *Hyloicus*. The forewings are dark gray with two bands of darker color and a few black lines across them. The hindwings are dark brown-gray with a light patch at the bottom.

Pachysphinx modesta Mounted adult male

Pachysphinx modesta Fourth instar larva shedding its skin

PHOTO BY PAUL E. STONE, MUNITH, MICHIGAN

Pachysphinx modesta Pupae

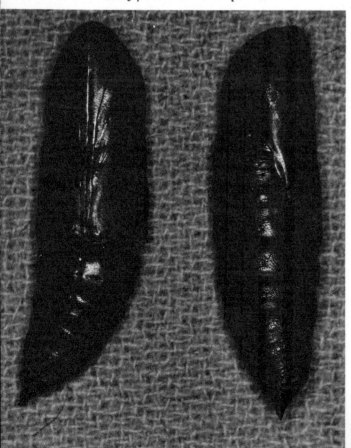

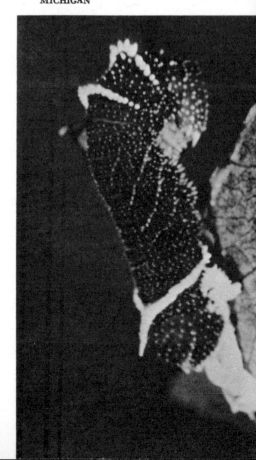

PACHYSPHINX MODESTA

Family   Sphingidae

Popular Name   Poplar Sphinx

Range   Most of the United States

Availability   Generally always available from domestic breeders, as well as from those in Europe.

Preferred Foodplant   Poplar

Accepted Alternate Foodplants   Willow

Diapause   Underground pupa

Ova   Typical sphingid egg—oval, green with a transparent shell.

Larvae   One of the most beautiful caterpillars we have in the United States. In the fourth instar, the body is deep olive green covered with raised dots of white and lighter olive. A ring of snow-white protuberances adorns two of the thoracic segments, and another ring at the rear extends into the horn.

Rearing Requirements   *Modesta,* being indigenous to most of the country, needs no special rearing condition, except that the cage or sleeve should be kept clean, and the inhabitants should not be overcrowded. Also, they sometimes take several days to molt and should not be disturbed when they are quiescent, awaiting the shedding of the skin.

Cocoon   The caterpillar goes underground a fair distance, spinning a very flimsy cocoon in which to pupate. The cocoon is really not worthy of the name, but merely serves to hold the earth around the cavity. The pupae are large, smooth with a pebbled surface and a bright chestnut-red color. The tail has a short but sharp spike and the pupa is umbilicate at the base of the spike. The wing cases are well defined.

Adult   One of our larger sphinx moths, *modesta* has olive-gray forewings with a light area covering the inner third and running across the thorax. There is a vague wavy line nearly centered in the darker portion of the wings. The hindwings are solid red-gray shading to cream at the inner margins. There is an indistinct black patch near the bottom center. Wingspan almost four inches.

Smerinthus ocellata Mounted adult female

Smerinthus ocellata Ova hatching. The little caterpillar has a tail a third as long as himself

Smerinthus ocellata Fifth instar larva. Looks
though the skin were beaded

SMERINTHUS OCELLATA

Family   Sphingidae

Popular Name   Eyed Hawk

Range   Europe

Availability   Generally available from most European dealers.

Preferred Foodplant   Willow

Accepted Alternate Foodplants   Poplar, Apple, and probably Cherry

Diapause   Subterranean pupa

Ova   Oval, medium sized, pale green.

Larvae   Pale green on hatching, with a pink forked horn. In the final instar the horn is long and sharp. The surface texture of the mature caterpillar is rough.

Rearing Requirements   As with most of the Sphinx moth caterpillars, nothing much in the way of special treatment is required. *Ocellata* likes to pupate near the base of a tree, probably to take advantage of the warmth there during the winter. Short sections of small tree trunks stuck into the pupating box should induce the caterpillars to group around them for pupating.

Cocoon   The pupa is smooth and shiny, fairly long and narrow. The color is very dark brown.

Adult   The forewings are gray patched and banded in brown. The hindwings are a pink-gray with a pale blue eye spot in the center. The eye spots are surrounded with paler rings.

Smerinthus planus Mounted adult male

Smerinthus planus A couple of these ova are infertile, but the indentation in the sides of the others is natural. The color is pale green and translucent

Smerinthus planus Caterpillars of *planus* beautifully pebbled on the surface, whic divided into very narrow ridges. Fifth insta

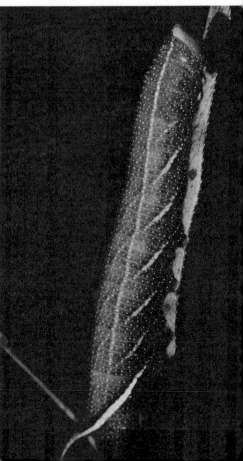

SMERINTHUS PLANUS

Family   Sphingidae

Popular Name   None to my knowledge

Range   Japan and the Indo-Asian region

Availability   Many European breeders now have established races of *planus* and offer eggs in season. Once in a while an American breeder has eggs.

Preferred Foodplant   Willow

Accepted Alternate Foodplants   Red Ozier, Poplar, White Ash, White Birch

Diapause   Pupa

Ova   Small ovals with an indentation on the sides. Pale green.

Larvae   An interesting caterpillar. The body is rich blue-green, covered with multitudinous narrow ridges encircling the animal. Each ring carries a row of small yellow protuberances. A faint yellow line runs the length of the body high on the sides and seven yellow stripes slant rearward on each side. The last stripe runs right up into the horn which turns to bright blue as it leaves the body.

Rearing Requirements   Plenty of fresh food and a large roomy cage seems to be all that is necessary to successfully bring this species to maturation. As in the case of most *Sphingid* moths they will flourish indoors if the food is kept fresh and succulent.

Cocoon   *Planus* goes underground a few inches to pupate, and does not make a cocoon of any note. The cavity is strengthened with a strand or two of silk and the pupa within is dark purple-brown. Smoothly surfaced and somewhat glossy. There is a short sharp spike at the tail end. The wing cases are clearly defined.

Adult   The forewings are raw umber with cryptic patches of pale sepia and brown. The hindwings are cream and tan with rose shading around the large ocelli. The ocelli have a sepia center ringed in pale lavender and surrounded in black. An umber line emarginates the hindwings. The thorax is pale sepia with a broad black line down the center. The abdomen is light brown, with no distinguishing markings. Wingspan about three inches.

Sphecodina abbottii Mounted adult female

Sphecodina abbottii Pupae

Sphecodina abbottii Fifth instar larva on twig

SPHECODINA ABBOTTII

Family   Sphingidae

Popular Name   Abbot's Sphinx

Range   Canada and the eastern United States, west to Kansas

Availability   The larvae can be collected wild. Dealers seldom have this very desirable species in stock.

Preferred Foodplant   Grape

Accepted Alternate Foodplants   Virginia Creeper

Diapause   Pupa

Ova   Small pale green translucent with a small dimple on the side, like most other sphingid eggs.

Larvae   A rather interesting caterpillar, naked, the body cream color with chestnut-red markings all over, making the animal remarkably resemble the bark of the vines it feeds upon.

Rearing Requirements   *Abbottii* needs nothing other than fresh food, and to be left undisturbed during the day, most of which time it remains quiescent along a portion of the vine stem. They feed at night, so fresh food should be given them in the late evening rather than in the morning, or during the day. The only specimens I have reared have been from wild caterpillars taken from vine stems of Virginia Creeper. Look for them low down near the ground, hugging the stem and colored so perfectly that you may cast your eyes over them a dozen times before you realize there is a caterpillar in front of you. The animal goes underground a short distance and does not make too solid a cocoon in which to pupate.

Cocoon   The pupae are fairly stout, deep red-chestnut in color, and shiny. The surface of the wing cases is slightly plicate. The abdominal segments are deeply indentate and there is a very sharp short spine at the tail.

Adult   One of our truly beautiful moths, and one which is very seldom seen. It is a small moth—not much over two inches in span. The forewings are beautifully crenulate on their outer margins and the cryptic markings of rich burnt umber tan and sepia swirl into the wing from the scallops. The hindwings have a wavy outer margin and the outer half is colored in burnt umber with wavy black lines running through the ground color. The inner, upper half of the hindwings is a bright golden-yellow. The body is a blend of umber and sepia with a black band or two. The tail is broadened out into a brush of pale tan bristles, and the abdominal segments carry truncated tufts of stiff hairs.

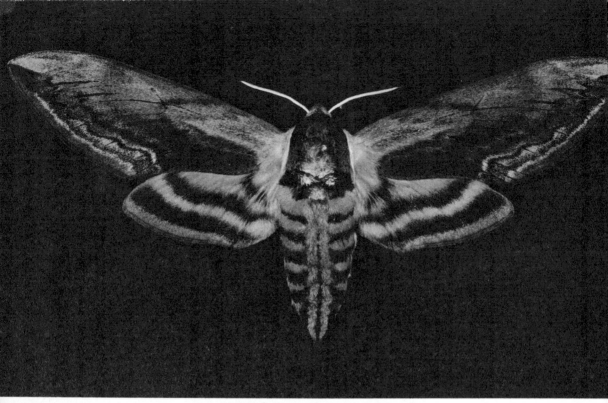

Sphinx ligustri Mounted adult female

Sphinx ligustri Fifth instar larva

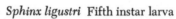

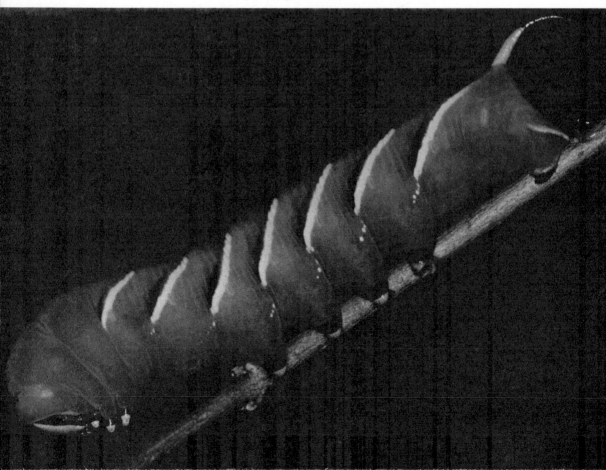

SPHINX LIGUSTRI

Family Sphingidae

Popular Name Privet Hawk

Range Central Europe

Availability Almost always obtainable from European breeders.

Preferred Foodplant Privet

Accepted Alternate Foodplants Lilac and Ash, and a few others

Diapause Pupa

Ova Medium, pale green, leaving a clear pearly shell after hatching.

Larvae Pale green, with enormously long horns when first hatched. The mature caterpillar is very beautiful. Smooth pale green with oblique enamel-white stripes on each side. These stripes are edged in violet in front, and pale yellow behind. As the caterpillar reaches the time of pupation, it turns a muddy red color and becomes very restless.

Rearing Requirements The caterpillars have large appetites, and need a lot of fresh food. They can tolerate a bit of crowding, but it is not good practice to do so. When they are ready to pupate a deep box must be supplied, because *ligustri* burrows down in the ground for several inches.

Cocoon The pupa is large, smooth and shiny, and colored dark red-brown. The abdominal segments are clearly defined, and the cremaster is short and sharp.

Adult The moth is one of the most beautiful of the sphingids. The forewings are cryptically marked in gray, brown, and black, diffused with pink. The hindwings are rosy pink with two undulating bands of black and an edging of sand. The body has alternated pink and black stripes with a sand-colored band down the center of the dorsal surface. Wingspan about three inches.

Actias artemis Mounted adult female. The hindwings are curiously truncated on the "tails"

Actias artemis Ova

Actias artemis Fifth instar larva

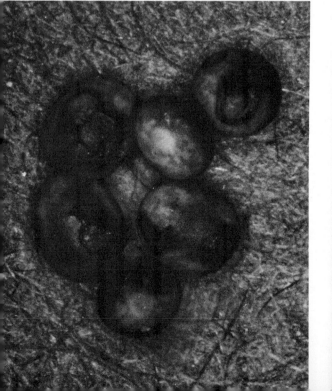

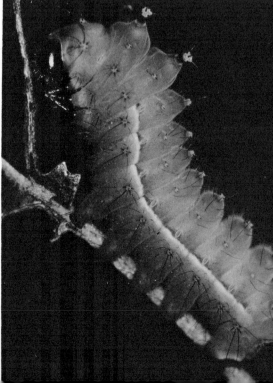

ACTIAS ARTEMIS

Family   Saturniidae

Popular Name   Japanese Moon Moth

Range   Japan and parts of Asia

Availability   Usually available from European dealers and from breeders in Japan, but not often on the American market.

Preferred Foodplant   Walnut

Accepted Alternate Foodplants   Cherry, Oak, Beech, Hickory, and possibly Chestnut

Diapause   Cocoon

Ova   Medium, white but almost entirely covered with black to brown mottling. Round, flattened spheres.

Larvae   Almost identical with *Actias selene,* except a little smaller. Body a shade of very pale green.

Rearing Requirements   None special. This species will thrive on cut food provided it is fresh. No special attention must be given to maintaining humid atmosphere, but a daily sprinkling is always good for them. Do very well on cut cherry indoors in medium to large cages.

Cocoon   Papery, in common with others of the genus. Generally wraps the cocoon in a leaf, which falls to the ground in the fall.

Adult   Colored very much the same as *selene,* the hindwings of this species are much foreshortened, and the processes are very abbreviated, especially in the females, wherein the tails are just short thick hook-like elongations turned straight out to the sides of the wings. Somewhat smaller than *selene,* about the size of our domestic luna, but more vividly and deeply colored than the latter species.

Actias selene Cocoon and naked pupa

Actias selene Fifth instar larva

Actias selene Ova

Actias selene The females have much longer "tails" on their rear wings. This is one of the largest of the *Actias* group

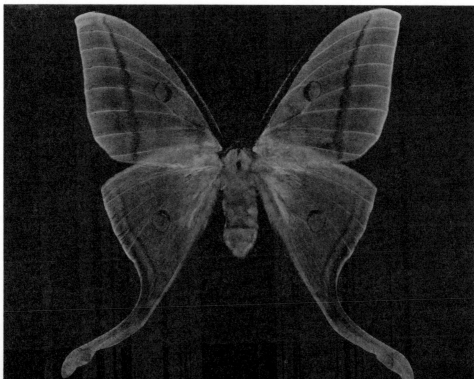

ACTIAS SELENE

Family   Saturniidae

Popular Name   Indian Moon Moth

Range   India

Availability   Generally readily available from all large breeders. In recent years this species has become more and more popular.

Preferred Foodplant   Rhododendron

Accepted Alternate Foodplants   Prunus, especially Apple and Cherry

Diapause   Cocoon, if kept cold after forming up the pupa inside. Otherwise this species can be continuously brooded if fed on Rhododendron right through the winter.

Ova   Very much like *Actias luna* except a little larger. White marked with black and brown. Rough appearing, oval.

Larvae   Large, fleshy, pale green, translucent body. Four yellow tubercles on the front segments, ringed with black, and studded with hairs. Body sparsely covered with long hairs. Spiracles orange. Claspers have a yellow and chestnut line across them. Size up to five inches if fed on natural foodplant.

Rearing Requirements   Need warmth and a humid atmosphere. The foodplants should be sprinkled with tepid water at least once a day, and a sprinkle on the caterpillars seems beneficial as well.

Cocoon   Large and papery, but rather tough. They usually are wrapped in a leaf, but may be made on the ground among the rubble beneath the tree. The pupa within is fat, succulent, and pale chestnut.

Adult   Pale aquamarine with a gray line down the forewings at the outer third. Eye spots large and pinkish with a black crescent on each spot. Costa is deep maroon. The long hindwing processes are yellowish at the ends, washed with rose slightly up into the wing area. Body large and snow-white, with a liberal cape of long white fur. Up to six inches across the forewings.

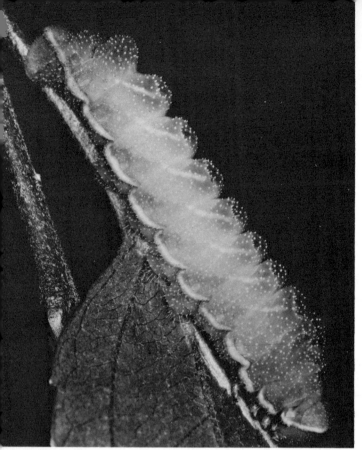

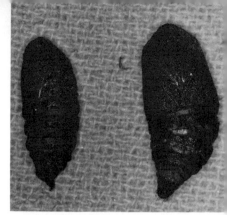

Aglia tau The pupa are short and rough on the surface. A brush of stiff bristles adorns the tail

Aglia tau The fifth instar larvae are translucent and look as though they are made of green wax

Aglia tau Ova

Aglia tau The wings of the adults have a soft fringe all around them. Adult male

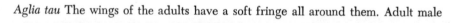

AGLIA TAU

Family   Saturniidae

Popular Name   None to my knowledge

Range   Japan to Europe

Availability   One or more of the European breeders will have *tau* each season. Rather rare in this country.

Preferred Foodplant   Birch

Accepted Alternate Foodplants   Beech, Lime, Sycamore, Oak, and Walnut

Diapause   Pupa

Ova   Large, pale brown, shaped like a flattened bean. Smooth and shiny.

Larvae   In the first instar, this is a truly striking caterpillar. It is fantastically armed with bifurcate spikes colored black, white, and red. From segment one, two of these spikes reach out forward over the head. Segment three bears another pair standing up stiffly. On the tenth segment another long spike points backward over the claspers. The segments in between are studded with shorter setae and hairs.

Rearing Requirements   This species requires lots of room and an airy condition. Preferably reared outdoors in large cages. If you crowd the caterpillars into a small space they will die. They lead sedentary and solitary lives.

Cocoon   This one's protection can hardly be called a cocoon. Spun up just below the surface of the ground, it is merely a few strands of silk. The pupa encases itself in moss or leaves, or in plain dirt.

Adult   Males are more orange and females more yellow. The forewings of the male are slightly processed at the tips. Eye spots are small and vary from round to oval. Two and one-half to three inches across.

Antheraea assamensis The forewings of *assamensis* are processed much like those of A. *yamamai*, to which this species is closely related

Antheraea assamensis Fourth instar larva

Antheraea assamensis Ova

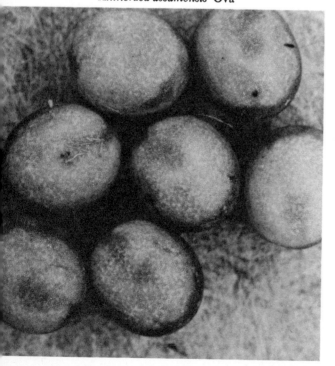

ANTHERAEA ASSAMENSIS (A. ASSAMI)

Family   Saturniidae

Popular Name   Muga Silk-Moth

Range   Assam to the Himalayas

Availability   European breeders offer eggs every once in a while.

Preferred Foodplant   Oak

Accepted Alternate Foodplants   None to my knowledge

Diapause   Ova

Ova   Large, flattened rounds.

Larvae   Hard to distinguish from many of the other *Antheraea* caterpillars. The body is succulent, deep transluscent green, with short stiff hairs sparsely scattered over the segments.

Rearing Requirements   Plenty of food, roomy quarters. This species does not take too well to crowding. Requires warmth and, if caged outdoors on growing plants, the cage or sleeve should be wrapped in plastic for additional warmth.

Cocoon   Fairly large, egg-shaped, no valve. Spun up amid the leaves of the tree on which the caterpillar fed.

Adult   Wings are light chestnut, with the costal region dusted with white. The eye spots are not hyaline. The wings of the males are strongly processed at the tips.

Antheraea mylitta The fifth instar larvae are like sausages

Antheraea mylitta Cocoons of *mylitta* are sometimes as large as a small egg

Antheraea mylitta Beautifully textured ova have decorative band around their periphery

Antheraea mylitta Mounted adult male

ANTHERAEA MYLITTA

Family   Saturniidae

Popular Name   Tusseh Silk-Moth

Range   Central India, Ceylon

Availability   A few dealers, especially in Europe and in England, have ova in season. However, several seasons may pass with no stock being offered for sale.

Preferred Foodplant   Oak—any species, but especially White Oak

Accepted Alternate Foodplants   Beech, Hornbeam

Diapause   Cocoon

Ova   Large flattened spheres, beautifully textured surface, with dark brown lines around the perimeter.

Larvae   The caterpillar of *A. mylitta* attains an enormous bulk, and has an appetite to match! It can exceed five inches in length and almost an inch in diameter. Pale green on top, and darker green below, with a yellow line between the two shades. Above the spiracles pearly lumps appear, which, when the caterpillar hangs upside down on a twig, look like drops of water.

Rearing Requirements   The larvae must have a very humid atmosphere in order to thrive. In fact, the wetter the better, as the coloration of the mature larvae suggests—dripping water. For this reason, a sleeve is not practical, and if cage-reared outdoors, unless you are resident in the tropics, the cage should be wrapped with a heavy clear plastic sheet, with just a small aperture at the top for ventilation. The growing bush may be sprinkled with a hose through the top vent at least once daily.

It is better to rear the species in a very large indoor cage, with plenty of room and plenty of fresh food, and sprinkle the food and the larvae at least three or four times daily. This will also necessitate cleaning the cage before each sprinkling, since the frass on the bottom of the cage will soak up the water and dissolve into a mass which will quickly mildew if not removed. I might suggest, however, that the species is well worth the extra time and trouble it takes to keep them healthy and happy.

Cocoon   The caterpillar spins its cocoon among the leaves, and is careful to weave a very strong peduncle around the branch to which the cocoon is attached. The cocoon is almost as large as a hen's egg, and is hardened by saturation from within by a chalky fluid.

Adult   The adult will emerge within a few weeks of spinning up if kept in a warm atmosphere. The cocoons should be sprinkled with tepid water at regular, frequent intervals. In its native habitat the species is continuously brooded, and, if you have access to Evergreen Oak or Holm Oak, there is every reason to believe that you could carry broods right through the winter.

The adult has a wingspan of almost six inches, and the females are much lighter in color and heavier than the males. The forewings of the male are processed quite a bit more than those of the female.

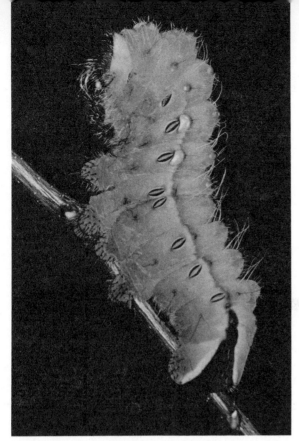

Antheraea paphia Cocoon spun among oak leaves

Antheraea paphia The fifth instar larva is difficult to distinguish from *Antheraea mylitta*

Antheraea paphia Ova

Antheraea paphia Paphia is thought by some persons to be a sub-species of *Antheraea mylitta*. Certainly it is very similar

ANTHERAEA PAPHIA

Family   Saturniidae

Popular Name   I do not know of any

Range   Indo-Asian Region

Availability   Generally one or another of the European breeders has eggs in season.

Preferred Foodplant   Oak

Accepted Alternate Foodplants   Possibly Willow, but I have had no success with anything but Oak of any species

Diapause   Cocoon

Ova   Very large, round, flattened globes. Yellow-tan in color with a slightly darker ring around the periphery. Granular surface.

Larvae   Almost impossible to distinguish from the caterpillars of *Antheraea mylitta*. (Some breeders think that *paphia* is a sub-species of *mylitta*, but Linnaeus puts it as a separate species.) The caterpillar is large, fleshy, translucent green. Body covered with short wiry hairs. There is a yellowish line running along the sides from about the third segment to the claspers, broadening out at the last two segments, then embracing a large dark vandyke brown triangle on the sides of the claspers. The spiracles are orange, rimmed with a fine black line. A blue dot is positioned on each segment both above and below each spiracle. Two rows of orange protuberances line the dorsal surface. Two pearly "water" drops adorn each side at the fourth and fifth segments. These are used as imitative or protective coloration in the same way as *Antheraea mylitta*.

Rearing Requirements   As with *mylitta*, *Antheraea paphia* requires a hot, humid atmosphere for its health and comfort. An outdoor cage should be wrapped in transparent plastic to keep out drafts, and the growing foodplant within should be liberally sprinkled each day. Crowding is not tolerated very well, since these animals are very large with corresponding appetites. The population density per cage should be low.

Cocoon   Almost as large as a hen's egg, the cocoon is attached to branches of the foodplants among the leaves by a very tough peduncle. The cocoon is saturated from within by a hardening fluid. There is no trap, or exit valve. The moth emerges by softening the cocoon with an enzyme, then biting through the top and pushing aside the cut silk strands.

Adult   Practically identical to *mylitta*, and every bit as large, but just a bit paler in overall color. The eye spots are large and round, hyaline. Body plump and bearing a thick cape of fur over the thorax.

Antheraea pernyi The cocoons of *pernyi* are hardened from within by the caterpillar. They are tan in color and quite large

Antheraea pernyi The easiest way to tell this species from others belonging to the genus *Antheraea* is by the tan, freckled head

Antheraea pernyi Ova

Antheraea pernyi Mounted adult female

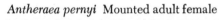

ANTHERAEA PERNYI

Family   Saturniidae

Popular Name   Chinese Oak Silk-Moth

Range   Southern China to Amurland

Availability   Generally always available, especially in Europe and the British Isles.

Preferred Foodplant   Oak

Accepted Alternate Foodplants   Birch, Hornbeam, Chestnut, and Plum

Diapause   Cocoon

Ova   Large flattish round, pale chestnut color, and smooth. Look like radish seeds.

Larvae   Large, pale green, sparsely covered with long yellowish hairs. Several pale blue spots on the sides of the first few segments, and a row of the same spots down the sides, one under each spiracle. The spiracles are chestnut, divided and ringed with yellow. Claspers are chestnut with a white stripe at the front. Head tan with brown freckles.

Rearing Requirements   Food—and more food—seems to be the only thing necessary to bring a brood of this species through to maturation. These are one of the easiest of all caterpillars to rear, and are ideal for the beginner. Feed them plenty of fresh oak leaves and you will raise ninety-nine percent of your caterpillars. They will stand crowding, which is not to say that you should deliberately do so. All larvae do better with more room. This one is also double brooded, given enough food and warmth.

Cocoon   Hard, tan, egg-shaped, with no trap or escape left in the spinning. After the cocoon is spun up, the caterpillar impregnates it from the inside with a hardening solution. The first brood will emerge in about ten days to two weeks after spinning, if kept in a dry warm location. About an hour before emergence the moth will secrete an enzyme which softens the silk on one end of the cocoon. This end will be wet and soft to the touch, and is an infallible sign of imminent emergence.

Adult   Large, tan, with wonderful feathery antennae like our domestic polyphemus moth. They are extremely easy to mate, and often will pair up immediately upon emergence even before they have fully expanded their wings, which may span as much as six inches.

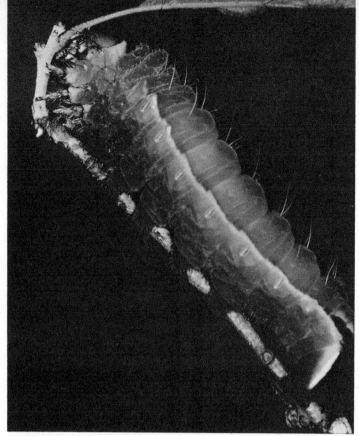

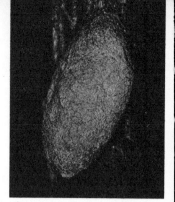

Antheraea yamamai The cocoon of *yamamai* is almost as large as a pullet egg. Like most of the cocoons of *Antheraea,* this one is hardened by impregnation by the caterpillar after spinning

Antheraea yamamai The caterpillars of *yamamai* are like sausages. This is the fifth, or final instar

Antheraea yamamai Ova

Antheraea yamamai Mounted adult male

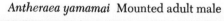

ANTHERAEA YAMAMAI

Family Saturniidae

Popular Name Japanese Oak Silk-Moth

Range Japan

Availability Always available in Europe. American breeders who import eggs from abroad generally have them to offer during the winter months.

Preferred Foodplant Oak

Accepted Alternate Foodplants None

Diapause Ova

Ova Large, oval, mottled black and brownish. Slight depression on the sides.

Larvae Large fat fleshy caterpillar, with bright blue spots scattered on the body. Head blue. Pearly to silver spots on the sides of the fourth and fifth segments. Sparse hairs over the body. The claspers are marked with a large triangle of deep chestnut lined with white in front. Pale yellow line from the third segment to the claspers.

Rearing Requirements *Yamamai* needs lots of space, and is better reared in outdoor cages or large sleeves. It sometimes hatches early before a good supply of food is available unless the eggs are kept refrigerated. When the oak buds start to open you can remove the eggs from the cold storage and set them out to hatch.

Cocoon Large, egg-shaped, and yellow. Look like lemons. Like *polyphemus* and *pernyi,* this moth leaves no escape hatch but softens the cocoon from the inside with an enzyme when ready to emerge.

Adult The males of this species are wonderfully varied. In a large brood, hardly any two will be colored alike. The females are all light yellow-brown, but the males vary from pale tan to deep orange, brown, and maroon. The forewings of the males are slightly processed.

Argema mittrei Mounted adult male

ARGEMA MITTREI

Family   Saturniidae

Popular Name   Giant Moth, Bat Moth

Range   Southern Madagascar

Availability   Until about three years ago, this was probably the rarest moth known. No one had successfully bred them, nor had anyone been able to rear any specimens. Foodplants were unknown. Otto Jancik in Furth-Göttweig, Austria, was the first known breeder to successfully pair them, but he was not the first to rear them. Almost every season now, he offers fertile eggs obtained from matings taken from emerging moths from wild-collected cocoons. Very costly.

Preferred Foodplant   Anybody's guess—see rearing requirements below

Accepted Alternate Foodplants   Pepper Tree (*Schinus molle*), Poison Ivy, Dwarf Sumac, Staghorn Sumac

Diapause   Cocoon

Ova   Truly giant. The eggs are pale muddy white, with no distinguishing markings. Round, flattened, spherical.

Larvae   Not nearly as large as the eventual size of the moth would indicate, because the body of the moth is very small in relation to the wing area (a phenomenon noted in several species of the giant moths). The segments are very deeply indented and the body is a beautiful translucent yellow-green with lighter yellow bands in the deep separations of the segments. Studded with fine short hairs. The spiracles are very small and pale in color. There is a sprinkling of pepper spots on the claspers.

Rearing Requirements   To the best of my knowledge, I was the first person to rear *mittrei* in the United States after I obtained two dozen eggs from Mr. Jancik from the mating of a pair of wild moths emerged from cocoons sent to him directly from Madagascar. The eggs were sent to me with the notation that no one knew the foodplants for the species. Previously I had done some research into the species in an attempt to discover the foodplant, but the only thing I could come up with was that the caterpillars fed on a "poisonous vine" in Madagascar.

On receipt of the eggs I set up twelve foodplant stations, each one containing four different species of food. When the eggs hatched, two caterpillars were placed into each brooder and carefully watched. One by one they expired, having refused to accept a single leaf. I tried trimming the edges of the leaves with cuticle scissors in an attempt to liberate the sap to start a chemical stimulus to feed, but this was not successful.

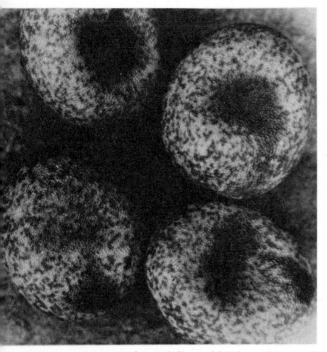

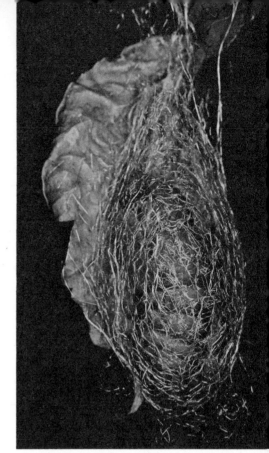

Argema mittrei A beautifully pebbled surface makes the eggs of *mittrei* interesting

Argema mittrei The lacework cocoon of species allows a clear view of the pupa w

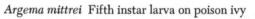

Argema mittrei Fifth instar larva on poison ivy

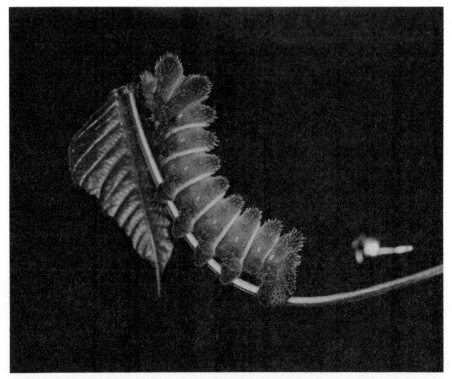

As each group died, they and the foodplants were discarded until the last brooder was reached. This one contained Dogbane (*Apocynum androsaemi-folium*), Poison Ivy (*Rhus toxicodendron*), Water Hemlock or Poison Parsnip (*Cicuta maculata*), and Mountain Laurel (*Kalmia latifolia*), sometimes called Poison Laurel—truly a toxic dining table. When the two larvae appeared dead I threw the foodplants away, examining them as usual. To my surprise the cater-pillars curled up as I touched them. The close examination of the foodplants disclosed a nibbling at the edges of the poison ivy leaves. I set up a new brooder with fresh poison ivy, trimming the edges of the leaves to allow flow of the oil from them. The caterpillars immediately began to feed and in two days molted their first skins. One larva, in its third instar, ate the stem away from the neck of the water container, walked down the remaining stems and drowned. The last one reached maturity, spun its cocoon and pupated successfully.

The following season Mr. Paul Stone of Munith, Michigan, reared one *mittrei* on a mixed diet of Dwarf Sumac and Staghorn Sumac (*Rhus copallina* and *R. typhina*). Mr. Paul W. Beard of Monterey, California, carried several to mat-uration on Pepper Tree (*Schinus molle*). There is still room for much work in rearing this most desirable species.

Cocoon Flimsy, openwork net of white silk, not hardened very much. The pupa can be clearly seen within. Suspended from the foodplant.

Adult Hardly anything need be told about this moth to breeders and collectors, since for years it has been the aim and goal of each to possess a specimen. The male has very long "tails" on the hindwings, those of the female being much shorter and stouter. The tails of the male are brown, dusted with gray. There is a dark patch on the tip of each forewing. The general overall color is deep orange-yellow. Two zig-zag lines divide the forewings in two, with a banded pale line near the attachment sides. Large ocelli adorn all four wings, rimmed in black with a small black spot in the center. Not hyaline. The costa is black, specked with gray, as is the outer edges of the hindwings leading down the tails. Ten to twelve inches from top to bottom, with a seven to eight inch wingspan. Females are wider, but shorter from top to bottom.

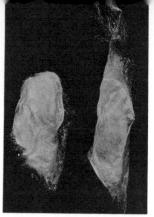

Attacus atlas edwardsi Cocoons. Sometimes they do not use a leaf wrapper

Attacus atlas edwardsi Fifth instar larva immediately after molting. This is the only time the true color of the larva can be seen

Attacus atlas edwardsi These ova are among the prettiest of moth eggs

Attacus atlas edwardsi Mounted adult male

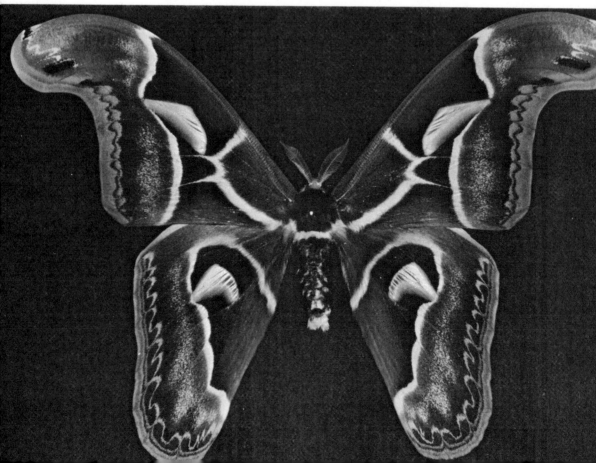

ATTACUS ATLAS EDWARDSI

Family   Saturniidae

Popular Name   Atlas Moth, Edward's Moth, Himalayan Silk-Moth

Range   Northern India

Availability   Generally always available from the large breeders, especially in Europe and Great Britain. Very popular species.

Preferred Foodplant   Privet. See rearing notes.

Accepted Alternate Foodplants   Plum, Apple, Poplar, and Willow

Diapause   Cocoon

Ova   Large, flattened rounds of dark cream color covered with deep chestnut mottlings.

Larvae   Large, fleshy caterpillar, covered with rows of fleshy, pale blue spines, but not urticating. The body is translucent greenish in color, with an orange patch on the claspers. Spiracles white. When nearing the time of molting, the entire body becomes covered with a sticky white opaque waxy secretion, entirely or almost entirely concealing the colors of the insect.

Rearing Requirements   *Edwardsi* needs a lot of fresh food, large quarters, and warmth. Humidity should be kept as high as possible. I rear them in cages over living shrubs, with a heavy plastic sheet tied around the sides of the cage, leaving the top open for ventilation; this makes a sort of hot house for the animals. In the later instars, the caterpillars should be given a mixture of several different kinds of foods. If they are being reared in cages, then the additional foods can be placed within the cage in containers of water, making very sure that all access to the water is plugged so the larvae will not walk down the stems and drown. The containers should be placed in the cage in such a manner that the new leaves are touching the growing plant and that the caterpillars can find their way from plant to plant, cafeteria style. Reared in this fashion, enormous caterpillars, almost five inches in length result, and the moths are beautiful and gigantic.

Cocoon   Surprisingly enough, the cocoon of such a large moth is small for what comes out of it. Long, tapering at both ends, with a not-too-well defined escape trap at the top end. White tangly silk is used in the making, and the caterpillar does not harden the cocoon from the inside. Spun up on branches of the foodplant.

Adult   This is one of the giant moths of the tropics, and is a great favorite of collectors and breeders. The colors of a freshly mounted specimen are deep and rich browns, magentas, and tans with gray, rose, and cream markings. The four triangular patches are hyaline and large. A well marked "Snake's Head" at the tips of the forewings. Bodies are small for the size of the moth, which may account for the comparatively small size of the cocoon.

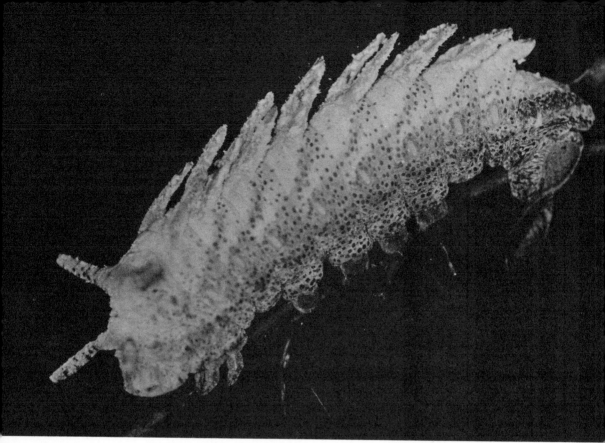

Attacus atlas formosanus Fifth instar larva shortly before pupating

Attacus atlas formosanus Mounted adult male

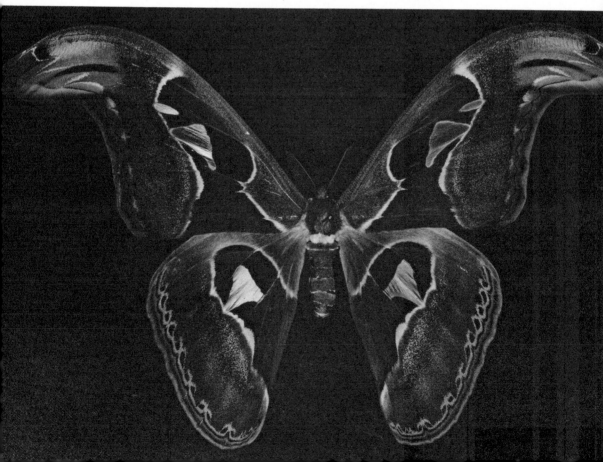

ATTACUS ATLAS FORMOSANUS

Family   Saturniidae

Popular Name   Atlas Moth, Atlas Silk-Moth

Range   Formosa, China, and surrounding area

Availability   Generally always available from Europe. Duke Downey in Sheridan, Wyoming, sometimes has them for sale, and on occasion Max Richter in East Durham, New York, can supply a few.

Preferred Foodplant   Privet

Accepted Alternate Foodplants   Ailanthus, Lilac, Apple and Cherry, Willow, Rhododendron, and possibly others

Diapause   Cocoon

Ova   Quite large round eggs, muddy white with dark purple stains. The female cements the eggs very firmly to the undersides of leaves, or on the side of the cage.

Larvae   The larvae of all the Atlas moths are very similar. They are fat, translucent green or blue with darker freckles on the fore segments. There are fleshy spines branching from each segment. The claspers usually carry a ring of orange, or a patch of the same color. Immediately after molting the caterpillar starts to cover its body with a sticky, white, waxy powder, which builds up until the entire caterpillar is heavily covered with it. The true color of the animal is almost hidden by this coating, and it strongly resembles the epiphytic roots of the plants among which it lives.

Rearing Requirements   The maintenance of heat and humidity is a must for the successful rearing of these animals. They like it hot and damp, and not too crowded. As the later instars approach, the animal likes to browse on a mixed diet of different plants. For this reason, if Atlas moths are to be reared with any sort of regularity, it is well to create a special ecological condition for them. Try planting a small specimen of several of the accepted foodplants tightly together in a group, so that the whole may be covered with a large sleeve or cage. Small privets, a lilac, started slips of apple and cherry all can be grouped together closely enough to be enclosed by the cage. In this way the caterpillars are allowed to feed on living trees rather than on cut food. They will do on cut food, but—in the case where the animal is used to a lush natural growth—it is far better to do what you can to give them living leaves.

Cocoon   Long and slender for the size of the moth that emerges from it. This is because the body is small in proportion to the wings, which are enormous. The cocoons are tan and are suspended from twigs of the foodplant by a very strong peduncle. Generally the cocoon is wrapped in a few leaves which are broken from the foodplant and used as sheathing for the exterior of the cocoon rather than as additional suspensories.

Adult   Truly this is a marvelous insect. The wings of a large female will span nearly a foot! The body is extremely small for the size of the moth. The color of the wings is a fairly even russet fading to lighter tan at the bases of each set. Large triangular hyaline areas adorn the wings. The tips of the forewings are strongly processed and have an astonishingly accurate image of a snake's head on them. The eye and mouth lines are very distinct. The hindwings have a scalloped line bordering them, faced with vandyke brown spots.

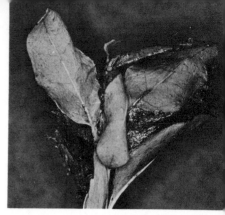

Automeris aurantiaca Cocoon

Automeris aurantiaca The fifth instar caterpillar is a thing of great beauty. The stiff bristles are severely urticating, however, and the larva must be handled with caution

Automeris aurantiaca Almost all ova of the g *Automeris* are white with a small dark micro This one is no exception

Automeris aurantiaca Mounted adult female

AUTOMERIS AURANTIACA

Family   Saturniidae

Popular Name   None to my knowledge

Range   South America

Availability   Up to recent years not readily obtainable, but the last two years have seen races established in England, so the larger breeders (such as World-wide Butterflies of Over Compton) should have eggs. I obtained my ova from Mr. Brian O. C. Gardiner, of Cambridge, England.

Preferred Foodplant   Privet

Accepted Alternate Foodplants   Lilac, Cherry, Willow, and others

Diapause   Cocoon

Ova   Fairly large, white with a dark micropyle.

Larvae   One of the truly beautiful tropical caterpillars. The body is pale taupe. The segments are pale green and from each springs a veritable forest of green spines, many-branched and urticating. A narrow white line crosses each segment, developing into a long triangle on the sides.

Rearing Requirements   As seems to be the case with all the species of *Automeris* that I have reared, the caterpillar takes the entire summer to mature. The feeding period is stretched on into the fall, until the breeder is hard put to keep fresh food available. It is an excellent idea to refrigerate leaves, as described on pg. 15 in the text, in order to have a supply ready if the larvae fail to spin up before the growing food becomes sere. It is mid-October, as I write this, and I still have caterpillars of *aurantiaca* slowly munching away. Others have already spun up their cocoons. All the specimens that remain in the larval stage have been brought inside into a heated room, and are being fed on privet, which is still green. They were started on lilac, on the 20th of May!

Cocoon   Spun up among the fallen leaves, or among the leaves on a branch of the foodplant. Wrapped in leaves, the cocoon is thin and papery, much like the cocoon of *Automeris io*. The color is light brown. The pupa is small and stout.

Adult   One of the smaller of the *Automeris* moths, but a real beauty, nonetheless. The forewings are plain purple-taupe with a light line running from the very tip across to the middle of the rear margin. The hindwings are the same ground color, with a very large ocellus, gray in the center, surrounded in black, then orange and again in black, this last black line being very narrow and wavy. Body is fat and thickly covered with hair. Span is about two inches for the male and a bit larger for the female.

Automeris io The caterpillar spins a thin, papery cocoon that is easily damaged if you are not careful

Automeris io Fifth instar larva. They urticate, so handle them with caution!

Automeris io The ova of *io* look like fa kernels of corn

Automeris io Mounted adult female

AUTOMERIS IO

Family   Saturniidae

Popular Name   Io moth, Eyed Moth

Range   The eastern half of the United States

Availability   Always available from one breeder or another. A very popular moth.

Preferred Foodplant   Wild Cherry, in my experience

Accepted Alternate Foodplants   Io will accept a great variety of foods. Willow, Box Elder, Poplar, Birch, Cotton, Corn, and Oak among them.

Diapause   Cocoon

Ova   Small, shaped much like a kernel of corn. Pure white with a pale micropyle at the time of deposit. The micropyle turns intense black within a day or so if the egg is fertile, but remains pale if infertile. A good indicator. The ova are laid in irregular patches.

Larvae   About two inches long, green, with a pink line running down the sides. Covered with clumps of stiff spines, this species is quite urticating and should be handled with care, especially by beginners.

   The caterpillar has the habit of curling up into a circle and dropping to the ground when disturbed.

Rearing Requirements   *Io* larvae can withstand conditions of crowding and otherwise uncomfortable surroundings, but this does not indicate that these should be the normal rearing arrangements. The caterpillar is in reality quite small, the bunches of spines making it look much larger than it is.

Cocoon   The cocoon of the Io moth is thin and papery, dark brown to pale tan, and is generally spun up among the fallen leaves at the base of the foodplant. I have found that an excellent way to obtain clean, easily-handled cocoons is to rear them in a large cage, in the bottom of which is placed four to six inches of pine needles. The caterpillars spin their cocoons among the needles (just under the surface) and they are easily sifted out of the bed for winter storage or sale. If reared in sleeves, they have an unfortunate tendency to spin among the fallen frass and, therefore, make the cocoons a bit difficult to handle.

Adult   The female is quite considerably larger than the male, and of a much lighter color. The male is dark brown with yellow markings and large eye spots on the hindwings. About two-inch wingspan. The female has almost twice the span and is deep yellow-orange in color, with very large eye spots on the hindwings. Pale mottlings of tan to brown over both wings.

Automeris leucane Cocoon, wrapped in leaves

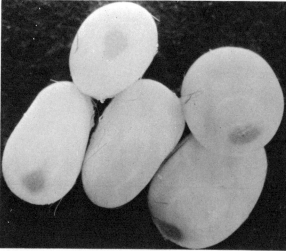

Automeris leucane Fifth instar larva on a plum leaf

Automeris leucane The ova of *leucane* are larger than many other *Automeris*

Automeris leucane Mounted adult female   PHOTO BY RAYMOND OSLAND, ENGLAND

AUTOMERIS LEUCANE

Family Saturniidae

Popular Name None known to me

Range Mexico and Central America, with an occasional straggler into the southwestern United States

Availability Not always available, but for the past three seasons several European dealers have offered the eggs for sale.

Preferred Foodplant Plum

Accepted Alternate Foodplants Lilac, Privet

Diapause Cocoon

Ova Small, oval, snow white, with a pale green micropyle. Takes several weeks to hatch, as do most ova of *Automeris* species.

Larvae In its final instar, the caterpillar of *leucane* is a beautiful animal indeed. Jet black and velvety, the first and last third of the body is covered with tufts of snow white spines, while the central portion is tufted in deep chrome yellow. Like all of the *Automeris* larvae, this one is severely urticating and should be handled with great care. *Leucane* is, in fact, so badly stinging that it is possible to become irritated just by brushing up against the sleeve or side of the cage. Also, among the *Automeris* group, *leucane* is no exception in that it seems to take forever to mature. All summer is not rare, and many times the larva will carry on into the fall until it is actually too cold for them to mature, and they will have to be brought inside where they can be kept warm until they spin up.

Rearing Requirements Fresh food and warm surroundings are musts for this species. They do not like to be crowded or windblown, and they should be protected from direct rain.

Cocoon This species spins a papery cocoon, wrapped in a leaf.

Adult One of the smaller of the *Automeris*, the moth has pale brown forewings with a dusting of pink on the outer edges, and a well defined line in about the outer third. The hindwings have an orange patch with a black ocellus in the center and two or three radiating, pale pink lines bordering the bottom of the wings. The forewings of *leucane* are processed slightly, and have a diagonal brown line across them dividing the wings roughly into halves, a tiny ocellus near the center. The body is plain brown. There is very little difference between the sexes except in size.

Bunea alcinoë Fifth instar larva

Bunea alcinoë Mounted adult male

BUNEA ALCINOË

Family   Saturniidae

Popular Name   None to my knowledge

Range   West Africa

Availability   Not often available. I obtained eggs from England one season, and saw them advertised two more times, but generally they are much sought after and hard to find. Worldwide Butterflies Ltd., Over Compton, Sherborne, Dorset, England, would be the best place to try for them.

Preferred Foodplant   Privet

Accepted Alternate Foodplants   Plum, Hawthorn, and possibly Apple and Cherry

Diapause   Deep subterranean pupa

Ova   Large, round, cream color, with a deep indentation at the micropyle.

Larvae   Deep red color, with spines like sharp thorns in eight rows down the body. The row just below the spiracles grows out of a black patch. Spiracles orange. Head black, and the spines from the second and third segments are black as well.

Rearing Requirements   Needs very fresh food, and prefers a warm humid atmosphere in the earlier instars. In the last instar it likes an airy environment. If the caterpillars are disturbed, they will lash their heads and front segments violently back and forth across the twig they are resting on. If one starts this motion, the rest will generally follow suit.

Cocoon   The larvae digs to a depth of four to six inches, and will bury itself in hard-packed soil! The pupa is rough and black. In their natural habitat, the pupae probably remain underground until the spring rains soften the soil. At any rate, after remaining dormant for a period, emergence may be induced by dipping the pupae in tepid water and keeping them damp for a short time.

Adult   The general overall color is deep purple-brown. There is a shaded patch along the inner third of the costa. The hyaline patch on the forewings is square shaped. Large ocelli adorn the hindwings. Two bands—one thin and the other quite broad—emarginate both pairs of wings about a quarter of the way in from the outer edges. The tips of the forewings are processed. Span well over six inches.

Caligula boisduvali Pupa and cocoon

Caligula boisduvali Fourth instar larva

Caligula boisduvali Ova

Caligula boisduvali Mounted adult female

CALIGULA BOISDUVALI

Family   Saturniidae

Popular Name   None to my knowledge

Range   Siberia to Japan

Availability   Always available from Japanese breeders, and generally from those in Europe. Sometimes Mr. Duke Downey, of Sheridan, Wyoming, offers eggs in the spring.

Preferred Foodplant   Apple

Accepted Alternate Foodplants   Cherry, Willow, Poplar, and many other deciduous trees

Diapause   Egg

Ova   Medium size, round. The ground color is gray with dark red-brown markings. A large micropyle turns black when hatching time draws near.

Larvae   Changes with each instar. Although black when hatched, the intermediate instars are green with a very dark brown-black dorsal stripe. The final instar is all green, and covered with short dense hairs making the caterpillar look like green plush.

Rearing Requirements   Nothing special. They are early feeders and one must watch out to see that the eggs do not hatch before the buds are opened, as is the case with many of the species that overwinter in the egg stage. A good practice is to keep the eggs refrigerated while you bring in branches to force the buds to open. As soon as green is showing on the opening buds you can bring out the eggs and allow them to warm up to room temperature. By the time they hatch, you should have young leaves showing in the buds and, by the time they are consumed, the buds should be open on the trees. It is good insurance, however, to start a second batch of forced branches at the time the eggs hatch, in case you have a late cold spell that would set the trees back a few days.

Cocoon   The cocoon of *boisduvali* is made of dark brown silk, and is not solid. The pupa can be dimly seen through the perforations of the cocoon, which is generally spun up among the leaves of the foodplant. The pupa is tan with dark wing cases and bands of very dark brown at the joints of the abdominal segments.

Adult   The overall color is dusty brown, with the forward third of the forewings white, dusted with brown. The ocelli are not hyaline and have a white band running through them and a border of dark brown. Vague, wavy brown lines run through the wings, and a wavy white band covers the inner half of the hindwings. There are some small black dots and lines on the apex. The whole of the markings makes the moth very attractive. Three-inch wingspan.

A sub-race *C. boisduvalu fallax* is marked the same way but is very much darker all over.

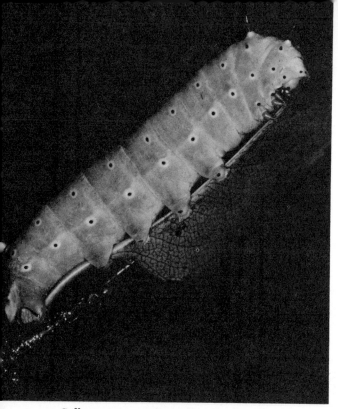

Callosamia promethea Fifth instar larva

Callosamia promethea Promethea cocoons generally made rolled up in a leaf. peduncle is tightly wrapped around the stem to secure the cocoon to the branch

Callosamia promethea Mounted adult female

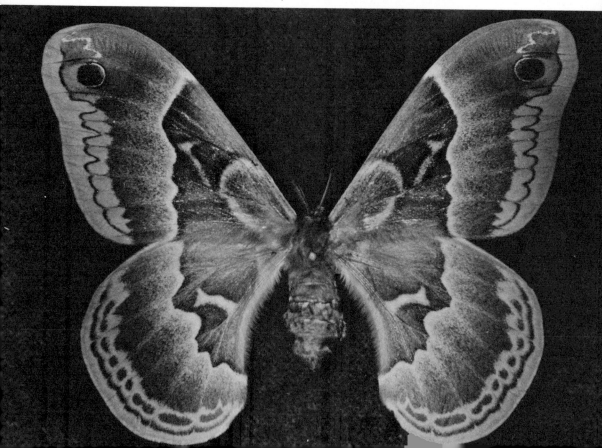

CALLOSAMIA PROMETHEA

Family   Saturniidae

Popular Name   Spicebush Silk-Moth

Range   The eastern half of the United States and Canada

Availability   Generally available from most American dealers and from a great number of dealers in Europe.

Preferred Foodplant   Spicebush and Wild Cherry

Accepted Alternate Foodplants   *Promethea* feeds on a number of plants, notably Lilac, Tulip Tree, Sweet Gum, Birch, Buttonbush, Prunus, Sassafras, and many others

Diapause   Cocoon

Ova   Small, white, flattened ovals. They are laid in a tight, curving row.

Larvae   Smooth, white, about two inches in length. Four tubercules rise from the fore part of the body in the fifth instar. In the first instar, *promethea* larvae feed gregariously in rows at the edge of the leaf, backing in toward the central vein, eating as they go. After the first or second molt they wander apart and lead more or less solitary lives until pupation.

Rearing Requirements   *Promethea* are hardy and healthy, and can be reared inside, in sleeves, or equally well in cages. I have found broods in sleeves to be relatively free from attacks of disease, but very prone to attack from Stinkbugs, who, finding a caterpillar on a leaf with its body touching the sleeve, will proceed to puncture the hapless larva right through the sleeve and suck it dry. In one season on the Butterfly Farm, the Stinkbugs were present in such numbers that I was forced to devise and use a system of double sleeves, with the outer one held away from the inner sleeve by a series of wire rings. This was successful in protecting broods from the predators.

Cocoon   The cocoon of *Callosamia promethea* is like that of *Philosamia cynthia*, with the latter being just a bit larger and not as silky in appearance. It is almost invariably spun up in a curled leaf, with a fairly strong attachment to the twig that serves to hold the cocoon onto the tree after the leaves have fallen. It is quite easy to collect wild cocoons by looking on the stark trees for remaining leaves, some of which are holding cocoons. I suppose it also makes it easy for parasitizing predators—such as wasps and certain flies—to find them too.

Adult   The *promethea* moth is an excellent example of sexual dichromatism. The females are considerably larger than the males, and are much more brightly colored, with cryptic wings. The males are smaller and very dark, some specimens being nearly melanistic.

Mating takes place in the late afternoon, from between 3:30 to 5:30 or 6:00 P.M. Sometimes several males will attempt to mate with the same female, and she is surrounded with a small cloud of flying insects. Wingspan about three to four inches.

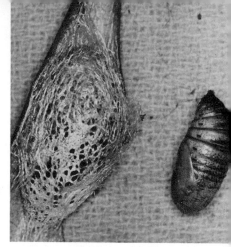

Cricula andrei Cocoon, and exposed pu[...]

Cricula andrei Fifth instar larva

Cricula andrei Ova

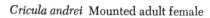

Cricula andrei Mounted adult female

CRICULA ANDREI

Family   Saturniidae

Popular Name   Scarlet Windowed Moth

Range   India

Availability   Nearly always available from European breeders, and sometimes offered by domestic collectors.

Preferred Foodplant   Hawthorn or Plum

Accepted Alternate Foodplants   Grape, Virginia Creeper, Lilac, Rhododendron, and Willow

Diapause   Cocoon

Ova   Medium sized, cream color with a greenish micropyle. Laid in sticky batches.

Larvae   Very beautiful. The caterpillar is pale apple-green dusted entirely with tiny yellow tubercules, interspersed with larger pink tubercules in regular rows along the body. Head tan. Short stiff hairs sparsely cover most of the body, with a few straggly longer black hairs on both ends.

Rearing Requirements   This is probably one of the easiest of all the tropical moths to rear. One bad feature about rearing *andrei* though is the lateness of the feeding span—until late fall. However, the larvae seem to be able to withstand a light frost without any difficulty, and, in fact, thrive on the chill evenings during the latter part of their feeding span. Another good feature about *andrei* is that it is not particular about which food it is given. The breeder can start it on plum, for instance, later changing to willow and then to any of the other accepted foodplants with little if any reluctance on the part of the animal to accept whatever is offered. In several broods I reared, they were started on privet and lilac. However, they took so long to feed that the leaves were getting sere and dry, so I transferred the entire broods to rhododendron, upon which the caterpillars finished their feeding and made their cocoons.

Cocoon   Pale golden-cream color, the cocoon is made of openwork net through which the pupa may be seen. The pupa is short, stout and a glistening tan-chestnut. The cocoon is generally wrapped in a leaf of the foodplant. The wing cases are clearly delineated. The abdominal segments are separated by darker brown bands. The surface of the pupa is covered with dark freckles, and there is a brush of short stiff hooked hairs at the tail.

Adult   The adult of *andrei* can hardly be distinguished from the adult *Cricula trifenestrata*. Perhaps *andrei* is a bit more subdued in coloration, with the bands less clearly delineated. The color is russet with the outer thirds of both wings shading to pink. Three perfectly clear spots are grouped together on each forewing, and one small, round hyaline area is on each hindwing. The band separating the pink area is wavy on the hindwings and straight on the forewings. Span about two and one-half to three inches.

Dirphia curitiba Mounted adult female

Dirphia curitiba The ova strongly resemble those of the *Automeris* moths

Dirphia curitiba The fifth instar larva is a formida[ble] creature. Very urticating

DIRPHIA CURITIBA

Family   Saturniidae

Popular Name   I do not know any

Range   South America

Availability   Very rare, and seldom available. However, European dealers sometimes offer eggs. Mr. Brian O. C. Gardiner, of Cambridge, England, I believe, was the first person to obtain stocks from South America, and very generously supplied me with some eggs. A race has been kept going in England, and either Mr. Gardiner or Worldwide Butterflies (also in England) might be able to supply eggs in season.

Preferred Foodplant   Oak

Accepted Alternate Foodplants   Black Locust, Walnut

Diapause   Cocoon

Ova   Large, oval, white with a dark spot surrounding the micropyle.

Larvae   In the final instar, this is a weird animal. The body is pale gray-blue, covered with a tracery of fine chestnut lines. The spination is truly formidable, consisting of a ring of stiff long spines around each segment, each one many-branched with short needles. This is one of the urticating species and should be handled with caution.

Other than the spine areas, the body is smooth. Just before pupating time the body turns a rusty, muddy red and the caterpillar becomes very restless, travelling endlessly around the bottom of the cage looking for a place to go underground.

Rearing Requirements   Perhaps the best description would be to quote an article sent me by Mr. Gardiner. "Having recently bred several members of this genus, I have found they are very particular about a pupation site, and I have always failed to obtain any pupae in a breeding cage. The following method, however, produces nearly one hundred percent success. Place about an inch of moist peat in a small tin box with a tightly fitting cover. (*Author's note*. A coffee can would be ideal.) On top of the peat, place a layer of moss. The larvae then pupate inside a tough, papery cocoon spun between the moss and the peat. Two larvae may be placed in each box, and they should be left at least three weeks before removal."

Cocoon   As stated above, this species makes a papery cocoon very similar to those of the genus *Automeris*. Incidentally, Mr. Gardiner's method really works, and a coffee can does just fine.

Adult   *Dirphia* is a large genus. *Curitiba* is one of the Calchas group, and is a medium-sized moth. The coloration is a little more obscure than that of most of the *Dirphias*. The forewings are light brown with a dark brown patch in the centers, and the hindwings are brown, fading to orange-brown with a few indistinct lines and an obscure ocellus. The abdomen is orange, with five black stripes marking the segments. There is a brown cape over the thorax. Wingspan a bit over three inches.

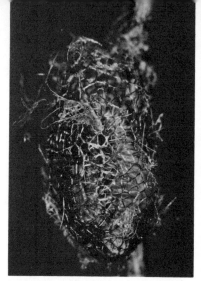

Dictyoploca japonica The pupating caterpillar may be clearly seen through the open mesh of the cocoon

Dictyoploca japonica Fifth instar larva. The most beautiful caterpillar I have ever reared

Dictyoploca japonica Even the ova of the species are pretty

Dictyoploca japonica Mounted adult female. The moth is not nearly as beautiful as its caterpillar

DICTYOPLOCA JAPONICA

Family   Saturniidae

Popular Name   None that I know

Range   Japan and Northern China

Availability   Always available from most European breeders and Japanese suppliers, and often from American dealers.

Preferred Foodplant   Cherry

Accepted Alternate Foodplants   Chestnut, Willow, Apple, Oak, and Hawthorn

Diapause   Egg

Ova   Oval, fairly large, blue-white mottled with brown. Has a large dark spot on one end.

Larvae   This species, together with the *Dictyoploca simla,* is among the most beautiful caterpillars I have ever reared. In the final instar the body is pale sepia broken with light dots. The surface appears granulated. Vandyke brown surrounds each of the spiracles, which are pale blue. The prolegs are tawny with the lower halves deep gold and covered with short yellow hairs. The anal claspers are speckled with vandyke brown, pale taupe, and gold spots. The dorsal surface is white and is densely covered with very long, luxuriant snow-white hairs springing erectly from the body like a mane.

Rearing Requirements   Although the prime food for this species is given as Cherry, I have always had best results rearing them on Oak. The caterpillars are quite active and somewhat gregarious. A curious habit that the larvae have in their earlier instars is to whip the forelength of their bodies back and forth when disturbed. Almost all the members of the brood will do this in unison. This motion is also practiced to a certain extent by *Bunea alcinoë. Japonica* may be reared outdoors, since the climate in its range is very like our own. This, together with the fact that its natural foods are common in this country, makes it imperative that the breeder take extra precaution against accidental—or deliberate—releasing of specimens. (While *Dictyoploca japonica* is not a pest moth, no species not indigenous to this country should be released for any reason whatsoever.)

Cocoon   About a week after reaching the fifth instar, *japonica* is ready to pupate. During this time the activity greatly diminishes, and the larvae become quite sedentary. The cocoon is an open network with the pupa clearly seen within. Immediately on forming, the pupa is bright green, but within a few hours becomes dark brown. They remain in the cocoon approximately a month, then emerge to lay their overwintering eggs.

Adult   The moth is very pretty with processed forewings. The overall color is dusty dark buff with a double wavy line running from the tip to the bottom edge of the forewings. A lighter patch of tan divides the forewings into thirds, and a narrow oval hyaline ocellus is on the outer edge of this area. The hindwings have a light stripe near the outer margin and the same wavy double line as the forewings. The ocelli are round, large, rimmed in dark brown with a black center shaded with gray. Sometimes the ocelli are rimmed in dark red instead of brown. Span about five and one-half inches.

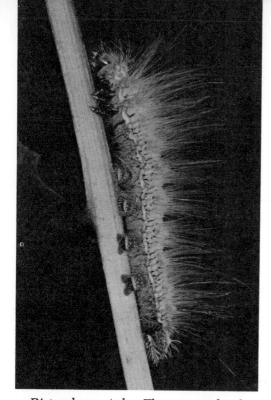

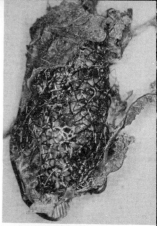

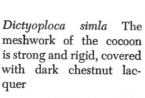
Dictyoploca simla The meshwork of the cocoon is strong and rigid, covered with dark chestnut lacquer

Dictyoploca simla The aqua-colored cape on this larva makes it a beautiful creature, indeed

Dictyoploca simla The ova are quite large for the genus

Dictyoploca simla The adults of this species are among the loveliest of all the *Antheraeas*. This is a male

DICTYOPLOCA SIMLA

Family   Saturniidae

Popular Name   I know of none

Range   Indo-Asian region

Availability   Not often available in this country. Sometimes sold by European breeders, especially in Germany and Austria. Otto Jancik in Austria generally has them each year.

Preferred Foodplant   Cherry

Accepted Alternate Foodplants   Willow, Apple, Pear

Diapause   Egg

Ova   The eggs are fairly large, dark mottled white. They are laid in even rows around twigs or on the bark of the foodplants.

Larvae   This species is erroneously called *Antheraea simla* by almost all breeders. Actually it is *Dictyoploca* and is very similar to *D. japonica*. The caterpillar is a beautiful thing, with a mane of long hairs of the palest aqua color. The sides are creamy white and there is a white dorsal stripe. The head is yellow, covered with white hairs. This species is also sometimes called *Caligula simla*.

Rearing Requirements   The larvae do not tolerate crowding very well, and prefer light airy conditions. They do very well caged outdoors on young cherry. If they are sleeved, they should be kept in sleeves of coarsely-meshed material. They can be reared indoors on cut food, but results leave much to be desired.

Cocoon   Like *Dictyoploca japonica*, the cocoon of simla is a beautiful open mesh, with the network strands varnished until they are stiff and glossy brown. The pupa may be clearly seen inside. The cocoon is attached to the branches of the foodplant among the leaves, and the adults emerge after a couple of weeks to mate and lay their eggs for the overwintering diapause.

Adult   The moth is somewhat plainly colored and drab. It has a white band behind the head. There is a round ocellus on each forewing that has a dark center. The surrounding patch is pale rather than hyaline. The wide costa is speckled gray. The wings lighten a bit toward the apex. About five- to six-inch wingspan.

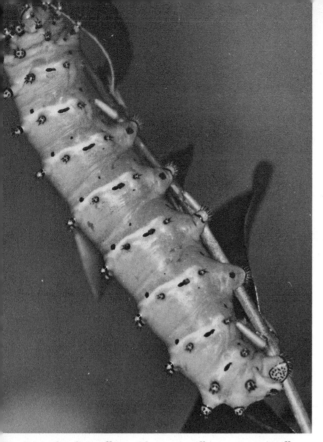

Eupackardia calletta The cocoons are neat and symmetrical, with a well-constructed emergence valve.

Eupackardia calletta The caterpillars are generally still feeding late in the season, and may have to be fed on refrigerated food.

Eupackardia calletta The ova have indents on their sides which make them look infertile at times.

Eupackardia calletta The adults of this species are diurnal and fly in the afternoon. This is the best time to mate them.

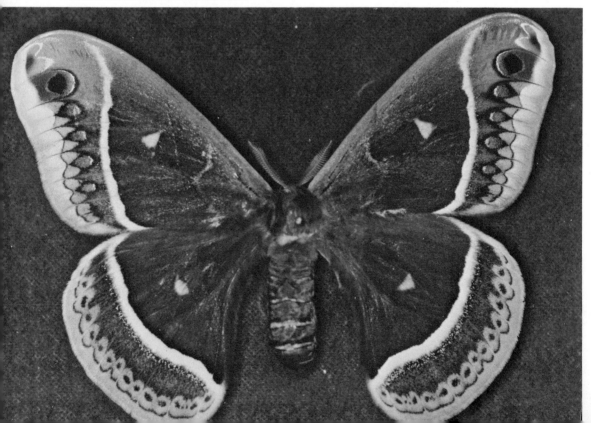

EUPACKARDIA CALLETA

Family Saturniidae

Popular Name None to my knowledge

Range Central and western portion of southern United States, Mexico into Central America

Availability While this is a fairly common species, the eggs and cocoons are not always available from most breeders. Every other year or so, someone will offer a few cocoons or some eggs.

Preferred Foodplant Depending upon their location, this animal feeds on Senecio, Wild Cherry, or Acacia

Accepted Alternate Foodplants *Calleta* will accept a number of different foods— Privet, Ash, Willow, Pepper Tree, Birch, Plum, and many others

Diapause Cocoon

Ova The eggs are large, chalky-white, laid in groups.

Larvae The caterpillars of this species strongly resemble those of the great *Hyalophora* group, except that they are a bit more gaudy. The predominant color is deep aqua, shading to greenish in the folds and fleshier portions. The spiracles are black and small. The protuberances are orange, with black club-like extensions. These are covered with short, stiff spines, also black, much like the studded head of a mace. The head is the same color as the body, with a vee-shaped orange stripe outlined in black. The claspers are orange, covered with black dots.

Rearing Requirements This is an easy species to rear in captivity if you have an abundance of fresh food available. Since the larvae do have a varied acceptance, it is possible to mix the foodplants into a sort of bouquet and allow the caterpillars to browse from one to the other, much in the manner of *Attacus edwardsi*. The caterpillars do need warmth and moisture to do well. This is easily obtained by a light sprinkle on the leaves of the foodplant two or three times each day. The caterpillars should not be soaked when the water is applied to the leaves. Sometimes a late brood can be brought to maturity on leaves that have been cut and stored in the refrigerator in plastic bags tightly sealed with the air expelled before sealing. Privet is the best material for this purpose.

Cocoon The cocoon of *calleta* is very neat and tight. It is attached to stems of the foodplant by a very strong peduncle, is tear-drop shaped and hardened from within after spinning. There is a very well-defined escape valve at the top, and the peduncle curves slightly over the valve.

Adult This is a dark, plainly colored moth, the males differing from the females only in size and a little in shape. The forewings of the males are processed a bit more strongly than those of the females. There are no ocelli; instead the wings each carry a small triangle of buff or light tan in contrast to the ground area of very dark sepia. A pale line divides the outer third of the wing area from the plain inner field. The outer edges are adorned with wavy lines, spots, and eye markings like the *Hyalophora* group.

Hemileuca maia Fifth instar larva

Hemileuca maia Mounted adult male

HEMILEUCA MAIA

Family   Saturniidae

Popular Name   Buck Moth

Range   Nova Scotia to Florida and westward to the Great Plains

Availability   Not generally offered by dealers, this is one of the species that can be collected easily in the wild. Look for egg rings on twigs of the foodplants, or try for gravid females to come to a collecting light.

Preferred Foodplant   Oak

Accepted Alternate Foodplants   Willow, Cherry, Hazel, and Poplar

Diapause   Egg or pupa

Ova   In neat rows around twigs of the foodplant. The female lays from one hundred to three hundred and fifty in each ring. Smooth, oval, olive-tan color.

Larvae   A wonderful animal. The body is black, thickly peppered with white dots. Each segment is ringed with tufts of short, barbed, stinging spines. Those on the dorsal area are brown and grow as radiating rosettes; the others are black with red bases and grow more or less in a tangle of severely urticating bristles. The prolegs are red. Handle this fellow with respect!

Rearing Requirements   Other than a supply of fresh food, nothing special is required to bring these caterpillars to maturation. They want it cool and airy, with some sunlight. However, they are gregarious and tend to bunch together on the branches. The larvae become very restless when pupating time arrives, and wander endlessly until the urge to dig underground overcomes them. They will often crawl into a crevice or under a rock in the pupating box and remain there for several days before searching out a place to pupate. They will generally come out during the warm midday period and wander about some more, hiding under the protection of the rock at night.

Cocoon   None to speak of; the caterpillars dig down a short distance in the soil and make their pupa in a cavity. Generally the adult will emerge in the fall of the same year, flying about in the sunlight during the hunting season. Hence the name "Buck Moth." Often, however, the pupa will remain dormant underground until the following fall, undergoing its diapause as the pupa instead of the egg. Those that emerge in the normal period of early fall will mate and lay their eggs on the foodplants. After the leaves have fallen, it is a fairly easy matter to search for the neat rings and clip the twig for winter storage.

Adult   Almost identical to that of *Hemileuca nevadensis* except that the white bands on the wings are considerably narrower in *maia* than in *nevadensis*. Both sets of wings are soft charcoal gray, with a narrow white band dividing them. In the hindwings a small black triangle with a white center is positioned in the white band near the leading edge. The forewings carry a white crescent rimmed in black in the white band near the costa. The antennae are feathery. Body dark gray. Wingspan two to two and one-half inches.

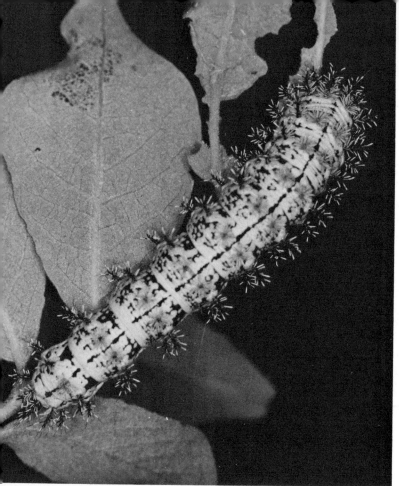

Hemileuca nevadensis Thre[e] different views of the pupa[

Hemileuca nevadensis Fifth instar larva. Bristly and urticating

Hemileuca nevadensis Neat egg rings are wrapped around a twig

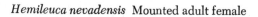

Hemileuca nevadensis Mounted adult female

HEMILEUCA NEVADENSIS

Family   Saturniidae

Popular Name   Nevada Buck Moth

Range   The western United States

Availability   Easier to collect wild egg rings than to depend upon supplies from breeders. Paul W. Beard, of Monterey, California, once collected several hundred rings in the matter of a couple of hours.

Preferred Foodplant   Willow

Accepted Alternate Foodplants   Oak, Cherry, and Hazel

Diapause   The egg *or* the adult

Ova   Olive-tan in color, they are neatly arranged in rings around twigs of the foodplants. Look exactly like olives stacked in a bottle.

Larvae   White body with small black markings and a broken black dorsal line. Each segment is patched with tufts of stinging bristles. The head is red.

Rearing Requirements   The caterpillars are gregarious and gather in bunches on the heavier branches of the foodplant. They are urticating and should be handled with care. There is no problem with crowding, since they all crowd together anyway, but the cage should be tightly closed because the larvae can escape through relatively small apertures. A cool, airy condition suits them best, but not full sunlight.

Cocoon   Spun up just under the ground. The pupa is short and stout, and has tiny sharp hooks on the tail end. The moth emerges in the fall about the time of the deer hunting season, hence the popular name of "Buck Moth." It is a day flying creature, and frequents groves of trees rather than open spaces. Sometimes the moth will enter the diapause in the pupal stage and overwinter in the cocoon, often until the following fall, but generally the adults emerge in the fall and deposit their eggs on twigs to overwinter.

Adult   A very pretty moth, but fairly small. About two inches or better in span. Resembles *Hemileuca maia,* to which it is closely related, but has a broader white band running through the middle of both sets of wings. There is a crescent-shaped ocellus in the center of the forewings near the costa, and a small triangular black spot on each hindwing. The rest of the wings and the body are rich gray. The tail end of the abdomen is brick red.

Hyalophora cecropia Ce-cropia cocoons are made in two styles. A fairly small cocoon is spun up among leaves. A quite large, baggy, soft cocoon is often made, with a smaller one inside. There seems to be no difference in the moths emerging from either kind of cocoon, however

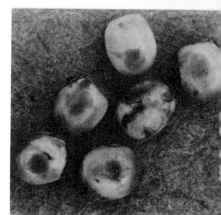

Hyalophora cecropia Four brightly colored, bristly knobs on the dorsum near the head distinguish this species. Most caterpillars of the genus *Hyalophora* have these knobs

Hyalophora cecropia Ova

Hyalophora cecropia Mounted adult male

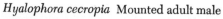

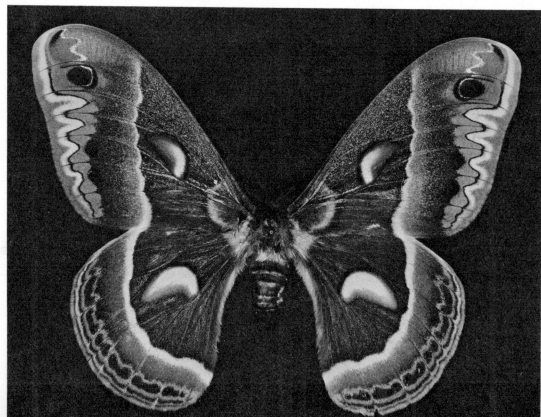

HYALOPHORA CECROPIA

Family   Saturniidae

Popular Name   Cecropia Moth. Robin Moth in England

Range   Most of the United States east of the Rocky Mountains

Availability   Very popular with beginners and breeders, and generally always readily available as ova in the spring and cocoons in the fall and winter.

Preferred Foodplant   I have had the best results and the largest caterpillars when I have used any of the species of Wild Cherry

Accepted Alternate Foodplants   *Cecropia* will accept a great many deciduous trees, among which are: Prunus, Box Elder, Willow, Alder, Pecan, Lilac, and many others

Diapause   Cocoon

Ova   The ova are large, oval, cream colored, covered with light red-bown mottlings. They have an indentation on the side. The female lays them in scattered patches on the leaves of the chosen foodplant.

Larvae   In the first instar they are black and covered with short bristles. In the final instar the caterpillar is enormous, greenish, with four orange tubercules on the thoracic segments, and many small blue and yellow tubercules on the other segments. In some species the four large tubercules are yellow or red, but these do not seem to carry through into any distinctive color variation in the adult.

Rearing Requirements   The young larvae are resistant to most disease and parasites, but as they enter into the fourth and final instar they seem to be prone to attack by disease. They are always choice prey to their predators, and great care must be taken to make certain that their cage or sleeve is tight and secure.

Because the caterpillar reaches an enormous size, and its appetite is in proportion to its growth, large cages covering an entire young tree are most desirable for raising a brood of any size. If sleeves are used, they must be as large as possible; the branch enclosed must be very full and bushy, and there should not be more than six to ten in a sleeve.

Cocoon   The *cecropia* moth spins two kinds of cocoons. A very large, somewhat loose and baggy one, and a small, tight and much more solid type. The kind or size of the cocoon does not seem to affect the size of the final adult. Generally the cocoons are attached to the trunk or the heavier branches of the food tree upon which the caterpillar fed. Sometimes, however, they will spin up in the fold of a sleeve instead of upon the branch.

Adult   This moth is one of the more dramatic in appearance, and when large and perfect is very beautiful. Wingspread often reaches an excess of six inches. An eye spot is present at the outer tips of the forewings, and there is a crescent-shaped hyaline area near the costa. The hindwings carry a larger hyaline area. The overall coloration is dark red-brown, sprinkled with silver-gray dusting on the forewings and pink on both wings. Antennae are heavily pectinated in the males.

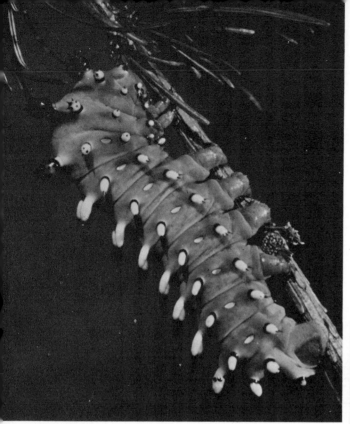

Hyalophora columbia The co-coons of *columbia* seem to be woven of gleaming silken strands. An escape valve is left at the upper end of each cocoon

Hyalophora columbia Fifth instar larva on larch
PHOTO COURTESY OF PAUL E. STONE, MUNITH, MICHIGAN

Hyalophora columbia The ova have flat sides are very beautifully marked with chestnut stains

Hyalophora columbia Mounted adult male

HYALOPHORA COLUMBIA

Family   Saturniidae

Popular Name   None to my knowledge

Range   According to Collins and Weast (*Wild Silk Moths of the United States*), *columbia* is found only in Michigan, Maine, and Wisconsin. Certainly it is not a common species.

Availability   Generally rare and unavailable, and the ova are quite costly when they are offered. The last ova I purchased were three dollars a dozen, and I was very happy to get them at this price!

Preferred Foodplant   Larch

Accepted Alternate Foodplants   None, except that Mr. Duke Downey of Sheridan, Wyoming, once reported that he had carried some *columbia* to maturity on Choke Cherry

Diapause   Cocoon

Ova   The same size, shape, and coloration as others in the same genus, e.g., *H. rubra, H. cecropia,* etc.

Larvae   Very beautiful, deep blue-green with bright red tubercules on the thoracic segments. The rest of the body is covered with small spiky tubercules. Reaches a length of about three inches, and is fat and chunky.

Rearing Requirements   My experience is that *columbia* cannot be reared indoors on cut food. The several times I have attempted this I have lost every larva after a week or two. Perhaps it is a matter of light and air as well as the fact that the food should be very fresh and succulent. When I have reared *columbia* inside large cages having small living larch trees, I have had almost total success. That is, out of a brood of fifty, forty-eight or forty-nine would reach maturity and spin up their cocoon.

Cocoon   Beautifully silky like that of *H. gloveri,* but even more pronounced in the silken weave. The young bark of a larch tree has a woven appearance, and the cocoon of *columbia* closely resembles this bark. Spun on branches and trunk of the food tree. A valve is left at the top.

Adult   One of the smallest of the *Hyalophora, columbia* very closely resembles the others of the genus but is much darker and purplish in color. A very desirable species to rear if you have access to growing larch, and one that has a ready sale in the form of ova or cocoons.

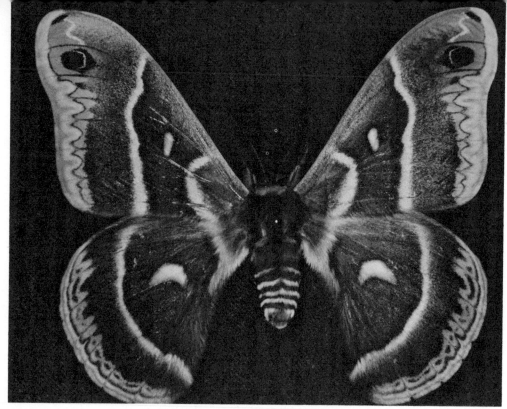

Hyalophora euryalis Mounted adult male

Hyalophora euryalis Cocoon. The caterpillar makes sure that its cocoon is securely fastened to the support

Hyalophora euryalis Second instar larvae o leaf

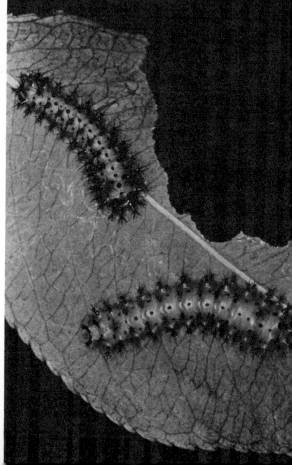

HYALOPHORA EURYALIS (H. RUBRA)

Family   Saturniidae

Popular Name   None to my knowledge

Range   The Pacific Coast of the United States and Canada

Availability   Not too commonly available, although ova or cocoons are offered in small quantities every other year or so.

Preferred Foodplant   Cat's claw (*Ceanothus thrysiflorus*)

Accepted Alternate Foodplants   *Euryalis* will accept Prunus. (I have successfully reared a brood on Wild Cherry, Willow, Apple, and Birch, although all the larvae I have obtained take Birch with great reluctance.) Collins and Weast report that the California Pepper trees are accepted as well as Manzanita.

Diapause   Cocoon

Ova   Much the same as *H. cecropia, H. gloveri,* and *H. columbia.*

Larvae   Very similar to *cecropia,* but smaller, and the thoracic tubercules are bright yellow in *euryalis.* The body tubercules are long and spiky. Caterpillar is light green, and very sluggish.

Rearing Requirements   *Euryalis* is very similar in its rearing conditions to *Hyalophora gloveri.* Either you can rear them or you can't, and it seems among the greater majority of European breeders, at least, that you can't. They seem to be very susceptible to disease and parasites. They should be sleeved or caged at a very low population density—not more than three or four to a six-foot sleeve on a leafy branch, or more than twelve or fourteen to a medium-sized cage over a bushy young tree. Watch out for parasites, especially Squashbugs and Stink-bugs. You should go over the tree or branch with a magnifying glass before introducing the eggs or larvae, to make absolutely certain that no predators are lurking among the leaves. It is a good practice to use double sleeves whenever possible to obviate attacks by the members of the shield-bug group.

Cocoon   The cocoon of *H. euryalis* is quite interesting. It is bottle-shaped, with a long neck and round body. The neck is the valve, and generally the cocoon is spun on a twig or branch with this valve free in the air and not touching the support. The cocoon is securely attached to the support.

Adults   *Euryalis* is a medium-sized moth, marked the same as the other members of the genus, but dark and redder in ground color. Wingspan close to six inches.

Hyalophora gloveri Mounted adult female

Hyalophora gloveri Ova

Hyalophora gloveri Third instar larva

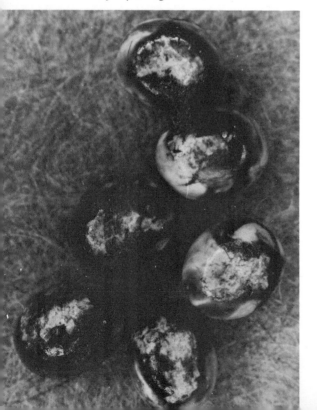

HYALOPHORA GLOVERI

Family Saturniidae

Popular Name None to my knowledge

Range The Rocky Mountain Chain from Canada to Mexico

Availability Not always available, and some years go by with no stocks offered by the breeders in this country. Often crosses are offered—*gloveri-cecropia*, *gloveri-rubra*, etc.

Preferred Foodplant Willow or Wild Cherry

Accepted Alternate Foodplants *Gloveri* is reported to accept Alder, Wild Currant, and Buffalo Berry (*Sheperdia*)

Diapause Cocoon

Ova Very similar to all the *Hyalophora* species—large flattened oval with an indent on the side, cream colored with brown or chestnut markings.

Larvae Very similar to the caterpillar of *Hyalophora cecropia*, but not attaining the great size of the latter. It is also darker in color, and the tubercules are not as prominent. The caterpillar seems to be very sluggish.

Rearing Requirements Either a breeder seems to be able to rear this species with no trouble, or else it seems impossible to carry a brood to maturity. Several breeders both here and in Europe report a dismal failure every time they attempt to rear *gloveri*, but I have reared several broods with no trouble at all by using Wild Cherry in large cages. On the other hand, three consecutive years resulted in complete failure for me as well. The only conclusion I can draw is that this species should be treated as though it were very delicate and temperamental, and that better than usual precautions should be taken against crowding, hot humid conditions, and disease. Disinfect the cage or sleeve before installing your brood, and watch closely for predators which will suck dry any larva which is so unfortunate as to touch the side of the cage or sleeve. Double sleeves will help reduce predation.

Cocoon The cocoon of *gloveri* is a beautiful thing. It is compact and light gray in color. Covered with a weave of silky strands, it looks as though it was woven out of loose silk ropes. There is a valve at the top, and the cocoon is spun on branches or the trunk of the foodplant.

Adult Smaller and quite considerably darker than *cecropia*, *gloveri* carries almost identical markings with this related species. Wingspan up to five inches or more.

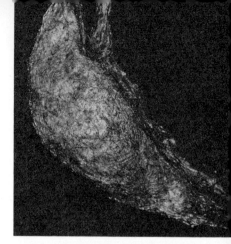

Loepa katinka Cocoon

Loepa katinka Fourth instar larvae on grape leaf

Loepa katinka Ova

Loepa katinka Mounted adult male

LOEPA KATINKA

Family   Saturniidae

Popular Name   Golden Emperor

Range   China and Northern India

Availability   Always available from European breeders, and often from domestic ones.

Preferred Foodplant   Virginia Creeper

Accepted Alternate Foodplants   Grape, Hawthorn

Diapause   Cocoon

Ova   Very pretty, medium flattened ovals, with a lovely surface texture. They are golden-brown in color, with self-colored smears in a darker shade.

Larvae   An unusual little animal. When it is in its defensive posture (which is most of the time, it seems), it very strongly resembles a clipped French Poodle. The extremely small head looks like the black shiny button-nose of the poodle. Covered with hairs so dark red as to appear almost black, the sides carry a row of intense triangles enclosing the spiracles. The triangles vary from sulphur-yellow to bright metallic aqua and contrast brilliantly with the body.

Rearing Requirements   About the only thing one must watch out for is the escape of the animals. They will easily walk through a hole you would swear nothing could penetrate. Once they get their button head through, the body will squeeze right after it. They do not like to be disturbed and are very timid. In fact, most of their time is spent in their defensive posture, emitting a bubble from just under the head which is part of their defense mechanism, I suppose. The forepart of the body is reared up over the abdomen with the head pointing straight down. At the slightest provocation all the inhabitants of the cage will assume this posture and hold it for several minutes. Another annoying habit they have is of dropping off the foodplant when you are changing the leaves. They can easily be lost in this manner, and great care must be taken when introducing fresh food.

Cocoon   Spun on a branch of the foodplant, it is well made of heavy silk and varies in color from yellow to green. There is a valve of straight hairs for emergence. The texture is papery, and there are indentations on the surface.

Adult   Wings are bright yellow, with wavy brown lines running across them from top to bottom. The ocelli are large and brown; those on the forewings are up touching the costa, while the ones on the hindwings are centered. Each ocellus has a darker brown crescent in its center. There is a faint scalloping of white at the outer margins of the wings. All together a very pretty specimen. The span is from two to three inches.

Nudaurelia cytheraea Fifth instar larva on Rhus glabra

Nudaurelia cytheraea Mounted adult male PHOTO BY RAYMOND OSLAND, ENGLAND

NUDAURELIA CYTHERAEA

Family   Saturniidae

Popular Name   None to my knowledge

Range   Africa

Availability   Some European breeders offer eggs once in a while. African stock is very scarce and hard to obtain, probably due to the political unrest on that continent. The eggs are scarce because there are very few good collectors.

Preferred Foodplant   Sumac (*Rhus glabra*)

Accepted Alternate Foodplants   Rose, Pine, Larch

Diapause   Deeply subterranean pupa

Ova   Round, white stained with dull brown. The surface is smooth and glossy. Medium large.

Larvae   When hatched, the caterpillar gives no indication of the dandy it grows up to become. The body is orange and there are numerous brown hairs springing from blackened spots on the segments. In the first instar, however, the animal is as gaudy as a beaded belt, and, in fact, strongly resembles that item of Indian apparel. The body is brick red.

Across the dorsal surfaces of the segments and banded along the lateral surfaces the entire caterpillar is studded with yellow, blue, and green "beads."

Rearing Requirements   This species is a slow feeder—that is, it takes a long time to mature, and it requires a hot humid condition in order to thrive. I had great difficulty in getting the newly hatched larvae to start feeding, and only after trimming the edges of the leaves did they respond to the chemical stimulus and start to consume the food. While in Europe *cytheraea* has been successfully reared on pine, rose, and larch, mine accepted nothing but *Rhus glabra*. It is very evident that all the known foodplants (known to me, that is) are substitutes and not the natural foodplant in the creature's normal environment. This lack of knowledge of foodplants for African species is one of the many drawbacks toward rearing specimens from the Dark Continent. It is a pity, because some of the most exotic and most beautiful species come from there.

Cocoon   *Cytheraea* digs down for a good distance underground before making a large cavity and lining it with frail silk. The pupa is short and stout and very dark in color. There is a very sharp spike at the tail end.

Adult   Some of the *Nudaurelias* are among the most beautiful moths of the world. *Cytheraea* is a fairly large one, wingspan being about four and one half inches. It is a pale orange-brown all over, with a central band bordered on the outside by a brown and gray line and on the inside by a brown and pink line. The forewings and rearwings have a hyaline ocellus surrounded by black, pink, and brown. None of these African moths are too plentiful. All of them are choice specimens for the collector or breeder, and are in great demand.

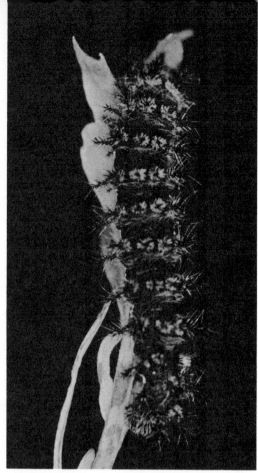

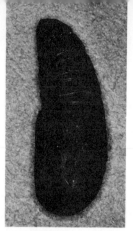

Pseudohazis   *hera*
Pupa

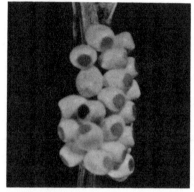

Pseudohazis hera Fifth instar larva on sagebrush

Pseudohazis hera The eggs of this species are carefully placed in rows around twigs of the foodplants

Pseudohazis hera Mounted adult male

PSEUDOHAZIS HERA

Family   Saturniidae

Popular Name   Holland calls it the Hera Moth

Range   The western desert states

Availability   Not often offered, but in its habitat may be taken in the later instars on the foodplant.

Preferred Foodplant   Sagebrush

Accepted Alternate Foodplants   None to my knowledge

Diapause   Egg, but often spends two years in the pupal stage

Ova   White, medium-sized ovals, laid in rings around twigs of the foodplant.

Larvae   Severely urticating, the body is black and the animal is tufted with barbed and bifurcated spines. Between the spiracles is an "S"-shaped line of cream. Rosettes of yellow spines rise from the dorsal surface of the segments.

Rearing Requirements   Unless you live in the desert section of the country, or close enough to the sagebrush country, it would be difficult to rear this specimen. They will accept cut food, but sagebrush is not easy to keep alive outside of its natural ecological setting.

Cocoon   Makes a flimsy cocoon among rubbish at the surface of the ground. The pupa is dull and rough, tapered for the whole length. No tail spike to speak of. Dark chestnut color.

Adult   Two color forms are common to this species, within which there is enormous variation. *Hera* has cream-colored wings with sharply delineated black or dark purple markings. Triangular wedges point inward around the outer periphery of both pairs of wings, pointing to and almost touching a wide black line vertically dividing the wing area. There is a shorter line crossing the wings near the body. The body is yellow on the abdomen, crossed by several black bands. Span nearly three inches.

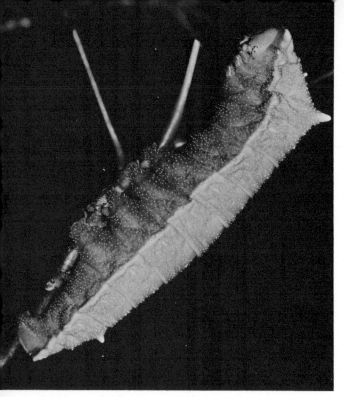

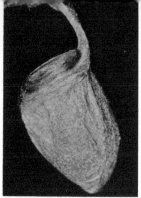

Rhodinia fugax Cocoon.
The valve is an open slit

Rhodinia fugax Fifth instar larva

Rhodinia fugax Ova hatching

Rhodinia fugax Mounted adult male

RHODINIA FUGAX

Family   Saturniidae

Popular Name   I do not know of any

Range   Japan and China

Availability   Almost every European breeder now offers eggs of this very popular species and some American breeders also sell them.

Preferred Foodplant   Chestnut

Accepted Alternate Foodplants   Oak, Plum, Sycamore, Black Alder, Cherry, Maple, and Hackberry (*Celtis*)

Diapause   Egg

Ova   Cream-ground heavily splotched with brown. Large rounded ovals, flattened on the sides.

Larvae   The caterpillar changes with each instar. In the final instar the body is green-yellow above, and yellow-green below. The line of demarcation runs just below the cream color spiracles, and there is a row of pale blue bumps spaced along the line, one on each segment. Four fleshy short spines protrude from the forequarters and two more from the rear. The body is curiously humped at the thoracic segments. The caterpillar emits faint squeakings when disturbed.

Rearing Requirements   Nothing special. The larvae accept so many kinds of plants that it is easy to rear them in captivity. They do not like hot humid conditions, however. In the last instar the foodplants given them should have several strong branches on them to provide locations for pupating.

Cocoon   The cocoon is as curious as the caterpillar. It is hung from the branches by a very strong peduncle attached to one side of the cocoon. The top is flat and open and the body pendulous and shaped something like a gourd. The color is yellow to green. While the caterpillar is spinning the cocoon, squeaks may be heard at frequent intervals, continuing after the cocoon has been completed and closed up. There is no seal in the top except a mat of loosely laid silk.

Adult   A very pretty moth, the females being somewhat reminiscent of *Loepa katinka*. Yellow wings, with obscure brown cryptic markings. The ocelli are hyaline and medium in size. The males are similar, except orange-brown ground color. The span is about three inches or more.

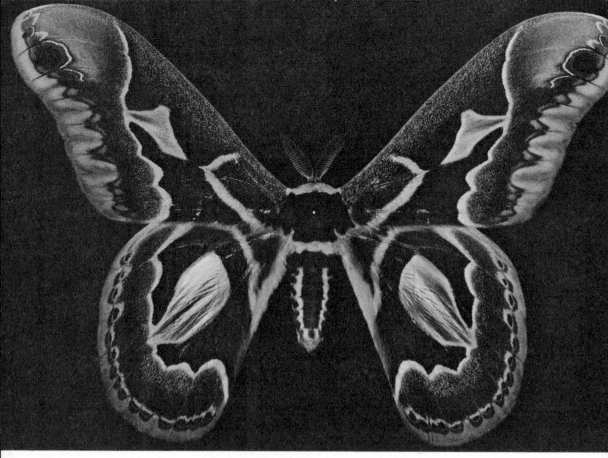

Rothschildia jacobaea Mounted adult male

Rothschildia jacobaea This is a trim, sleek cocoon with a
well-developed escape valve. A large amount of silk is
spun around the branches to hold the cocoon in place

Rothschildia jacobaea Fifth instar larva

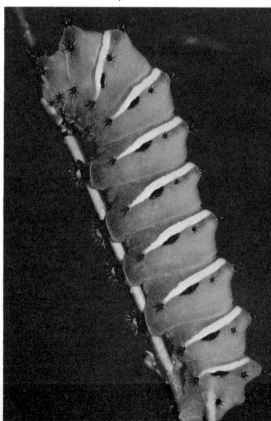

ROTHSCHILDIA JACOBAEA

Family   Saturniidae

Popular Name   None

Range   Argentina

Availability   Most European breeders have the eggs. Occasionally a breeder in this country offers stock.

Preferred Foodplant   Privet

Accepted Alternate Foodplants   Possibly Lilac

Diapause   Cocoon

Ova   Large flattened round. Glossy, creamy color.

Larvae   In the final instar the body is yellow-green with the segments deeply ridged and an enamel white line ringing each segment just in front of the spiracles. The spiracles are black. The prolegs are orange and the claspers are crimson rimmed in black. Round shiny tubercules spot the segments, and short stiff black spines branch out from each tubercule.

Rearing Requirements   This species needs a large cage and no overcrowding. The caterpillars get to be very large and plump and have corresponding appetites, so feed them accordingly. Very phlegmatic and docile, nothing much seems to disturb the larvae of most of the *Rothschildias*. When the caterpillar is ready to pupate, the enamel-white stripes turn a deep yellow or orange. The animal starts to spin almost as soon as this color change takes place.

Cocoon   Large, brownish, and tightly woven of tough silk, the cocoon is spun up among the leaves of the foodplant, and strongly attached to the branch. There is a relatively long valve. The cocoon is tapered towards both ends and has double walls, the inner chamber being much smaller and suspended within the large outer sheath by a mass of curled silken strands.

Adult   A typical *Rothschildia,* and a very pretty one. The genus is very closely related to *Attacus,* and is sometimes so called, especially by European breeders. The wing spots are hyaline and very large, those on the forewings being triangular and on the rearwings elongated ovals. The ground color is rich plum brown with a suggestion of gray dusting along the costal area. A scalloped black line bordered in white vertically divides both pairs of wings. The margins are tan with darker markings and the hindwings are emarginated by a row of dark brown spots enclosed in lighter scallops. The body is deep rose with cream bars and lines.

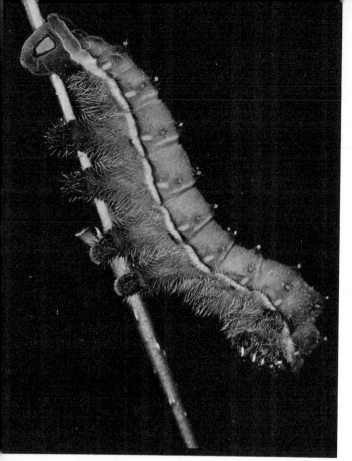

Rothschildia orizaba These cocoons are often completely covered with the leaves of the foodplant

Rothschildia orizaba Fifth instar larva

Rothschildia orizaba The eggs are laid in neat rows

Rothschildia orizaba Mounted adult male

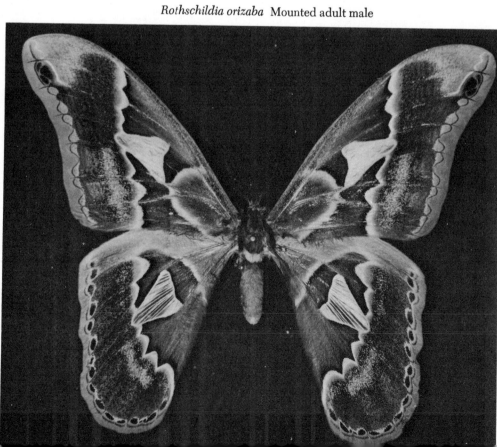

ROTHSCHILDIA ORIZABA

Family   Saturniidae

Popular Name   None to my knowledge

Range   Southern Mexico to South America

Availability   At least every couple of years ova or cocoons of *orizaba* are offered for sale by the larger breeders, especially the ones in Europe.

Preferred Foodplant   Privet, Pepper Tree (*Schinus molle*)

Accepted Alternate Foodplants   Ash, Willow, Lilac, and several others have been used with varying amounts of success. Also Cherry, both wild and cultivated.

Diapause   Cocoon

Ova   Medium large, bean-shaped, white. Laid in curving rows with each egg touching its neighbor.

Larvae   Large and chunky. Two-toned green, paler and smooth on the back, with sparse small tubercules. A line in the middle of the sides divides the smooth top section from the hirsute bottom part. The caterpillar looks as though it is covered with short dark green fur on the lower half. Slightly urticating.

Rearing Requirements   I have only reared this species on Privet, and find that they take to this food readily and reach good size. They do not like to be crowded. They will accept cut food but seem to prefer fresh growing plants, and, in fact, attain better growth at a faster rate on a growing privet bush than indoors on cut branches. They also seem to be able to withstand hot and humid conditions. Probably this approximates the natural climate in their native habitat.

Cocoon   Similar to *Samia cynthia*. The cocoon is suspended by a flat peduncle from the twig of the foodplant. It has a valve.

Adult   This is a beautiful, large moth with a wingspan of five to six inches. Each wing carries a large triangular clear patch that opens into the dark scalloped dividing line that separates the wing down the middle from a dusted outer margin. Light brown, this specimen tends to fade or bleach out considerably after mounting if it is kept in strong light.

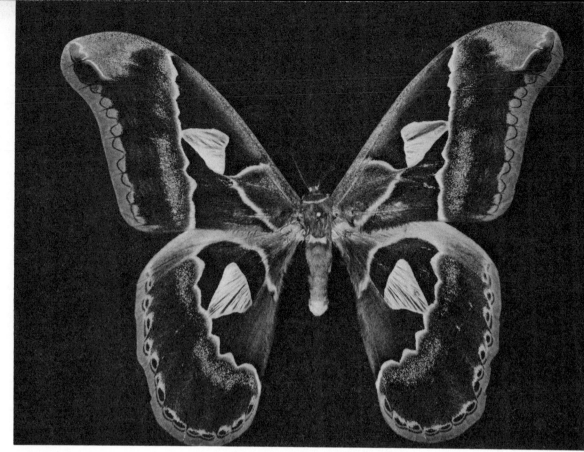

Rothschildia speculifera Mounted adult male

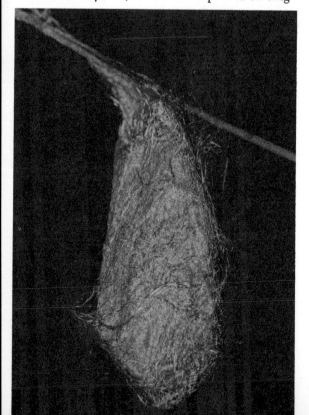

Rothschildia speculifera Cocoon suspended on twig

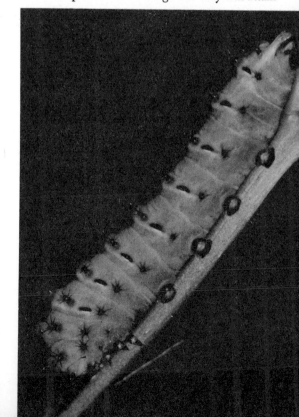

Rothschildia speculifera Third instar larvae alre
show promise of the large size they will attain

ROTHSCHILDIA SPECULIFERA

Family Saturniidae

Popular Name None

Range South America

Availability From European dealers. Once in a while from domestic dealers, but not often.

Preferred Foodplant Privet

Accepted Alternate Foodplants Wild Cherry, Lilac, Buttonbush, and Ash

Diapause Cocoon

Ova Large, white, smooth, laid in patches.

Larvae Body a green-orange, with black tubercules from the segments of which spring short, stinging, black spines. True legs, prolegs, and claspers are all black with a bright orange center. Spiracles are black, rimmed in front with yellow.

Rearing Requirements Likes it warm and dry, with an occasional sprinkle of tepid water on the leaves. The newly hatched larvae must be kept out of drafts and in a humid atmosphere. Large caterpillars, with large appetites, they need very fresh food.

Cocoon A slightly messy type with a lot of loose silk on the outside. A valve of sorts at the top, which is attached close to the branch by a short peduncle. The cocoon is generally wrapped in leaves of the foodplant.

Adult I think this is the prettiest of the *Rothschildias*. The inner half of both sets of wings is red-brown with a pink-brown area connecting the wings to the thorax. This is bordered in white, then black. A wavy black line, bordered in white, delineates a patch of delicate rose dusted with gray and fading into tan toward the outer margin, which becomes puce with a row of brown spots enclosed in lighter scallops. The hyaline areas are triangular and large; the outer tips of the triangles touch the border line of the red-brown central color. The forewing tips are very slightly processed. A wide white band separates the thorax from the abdomen. Wingspan nearly five inches.

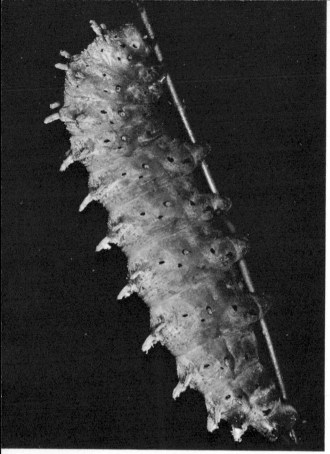

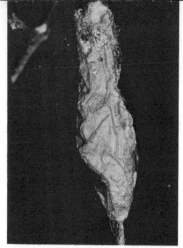

Samia cynthia Cocoon

Samia cynthia The ova are like fancy Easter eggs

Samia cynthia The fifth instar larvae resemble the caterpillars of *Attacus atlas,* to which *cynthia* is related

Samia cynthia Mounted adult male

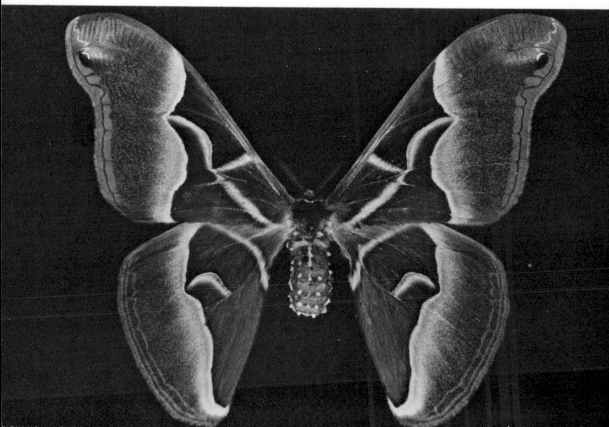

SAMIA (PHILOSAMIA) CYNTHIA

Family Saturniidae

Popular Name Ailanthus Moth, in the United States and India

Range Indigenous to China. Found generally widespread throughout Asia. *Philosamia cynthia* is now established in many countries throught the world, each country calling their race by a different subspecific name.

Availability Readily available in either cocoon or egg stage from almost every dealer

Preferred Foodplant In the United States, *Ailanthus* is the preferred food

Accepted Alternate Foodplants Privet, Lilac, Prunus, and some others are readily accepted

Diapause Cocoon

Ova Oval, plump, cream colored and nicely speckled with chestnut. Laid in rows or groups.

Larvae The larvae of *cynthia* resemble those of *Attacus*, in that, after the first two instars, the caterpillar is covered with a white powdery wax, and generally shows rows of black spots all over the body. However, the caterpillars are quite variable, and some may show no black at all while others have stripes instead of dots; the degree of coverage by the powder may also vary.

Rearing Requirements Nothing very special is required for *cynthia*, which succeeds admirably in adapting to whatever climate and ecological condition it finds itself in. The caterpillars do equally well in sleeves, cages, or indoors on cut food. They are quite sedentary and can stand a moderate amount of crowding, but that is not to say that caterpillars jammed together in a cage can be expected to thrive.

Cocoon The cocoon is spun up among the leaves, generally inside a leaf or two that are wrapped in a spiral around the cocoon. A strong peduncle is woven, and the cocoon is made with a valve for emergence. Cocoons of *cynthia* are quite considerably smaller than one would expect, judging from the final size of the caterpillar.

Adult The imago is very pretty, being brown with white crescents on each wing, shades of pink, cream, and tan. There is the merest suggestion of the *Attacus* "Snake Head" on the processes of the forewings, this illusion being increased by the presence of a small eye spot. Wingspan about five inches, but diminutive specimens are not rare, and a real giant is sometimes encountered.

Saturnia pavonia The cocoon is str⟨...⟩ made and has an emergence valve

Saturnia pavonia The larvae are differently colored and marked in each instar. This is the fifth instar just before pupating.

Saturnia pavonia Ova on the back of a leaf

Saturnia pavonia Mounted adult male. This species has the distinction of being the only Saturnid in the British Isles

SATURNIA PAVONIA

Family Saturniidae

Popular Name In Great Britain, the Emperor Moth

Range Great Britain and parts of Europe

Availability Almost every European and British breeder offers ova or cocoons of this popular species each season.

Preferred Foodplant Hawthorn

Accepted Alternate Foodplants This species accepts many trees and shrubs, including Blackberry, Raspberry, Willow, Apple, and Birch

Diapause Cocoon

Ova Grayish, oval, medium sized. Laid on undersides of leaves of the foodplant.

Larvae Variable in each of its instars. When hatched it is black and covered with spines. In the final instar it is bright blue-green on the body, ringed on each segment with black; the rings bear prominent tubercules, which, in turn, are set with tufts of black spines.

Rearing Requirements Nothing special. This is a very easy moth to rear if you have enough fresh food and do not overcrowd the larvae.

Cocoon Bottle shaped, with a valve. Spun up among the foliage of the foodplant, or among the leaves of a nearby plant. This species will often remain in the cocoon for two years before emerging.

Adult A very pretty moth, with cryptic coloration of both wings. All wings carry an eye spot in the center. The general overall color is warm brown and dusty gray, the latter color more prominent in the female. Patches of white to cream relieve the monotony of the brown.

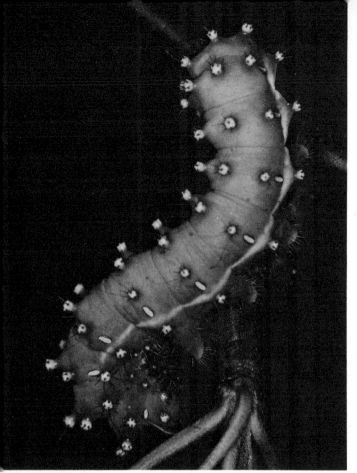

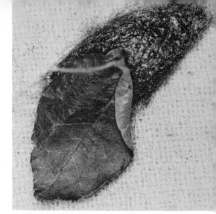

Saturnia pyri Cocoon wrapped in a l‹

Saturnia pyri The fifth instar larva is a beauty

Saturnia pyri Ova

Saturnia pyri Mounted adult male

SATURNIA PYRI

Family Saturniidae

Popular Name Great Peacock Moth

Range Southern Europe, Portugal, and the Near East to Iran

Availability Almost always available from European breeders. Sometimes available from breeders in the United States.

Preferred Foodplant Pear

Accepted Alternate Foodplants Apple, Ash, Privet, Cherry, Birch, Plum and Hops, Elm, Horse-Chestnut, Lime (*Tilia*), and Poplar

Diapause Cocoon

Ova Large flattened ovals. Dirty white with green and pale brown stains.

Larva The body is pale yellow-green, and the tubercules are very pale blue. From the tubercules spring many very long curved hairs, each one paddle-shaped at the outer end. A faint yellow line runs along the sides below the cream-colored spiracles.

Rearing Requirements Here is a species that takes a little patience to rear. It cannot tolerate dampness, and, in fact, requires almost desert conditions. These animals cannot be reared outdoors unless you can keep them in direct, hot sunlight and in airy cages. If these needs cannot be met, or if you cannot keep the cage hot and dry with the aid of artificial heaters or other mechanical devices, it is better that you do not attempt breeding this species, rather than let the animals languish and die.

Cocoon Brown, loosely woven of coarse silk, and generally wrapped in a leaf of the foodplant. The top is valved and there is an inner cocoon of tighter weave in which the animal pupates. The cocoon is most often spun flat against the trunk of the tree, but it is sometimes spun under overhanging ledges or loose bark. In the cage, the caterpillar shows a proclivity towards spinning at the juncture of the glass sides or the door, effectively locking it shut!

Adult In order for this moth to emerge and expand, the temperature must be kept near sixty-five degrees. Otherwise, the adult may remain in the cocoon for as long as two years. The cocoons must be sprinkled with water several times a day and kept at the same temperature as the surrounding air, or the emerging moth will be unable to get beyond the valve to properly expand its wings.

The wide and silver-white costa extends over the body in a white collar. The forewings are chocolate brown with wavy tan and umber lines. The margins are puce with a cream shading on their inner sides. The round ocelli are burnt umber surrounded with raw umber. On the inner sides of the body a white crescent is bordered with crimson. The body is fat and covered with thick hairs. Raw umber color with grayed bands marking the abdominal segments. Wingspan four inches or larger.

Telea polyphemus Cocoon

Telea polyphemus Fifth instar larva

Telea polyphemus Ova

Telea polyphemus Mounted adult male

TELEA POLYPHEMUS

Family Saturniidae

Popular Name Polyphemus Moth

Range Throughout the United States, into Canada

Availability Always available. A favorite of breeders and beginners because of the ease of rearing and the size of the caterpillar and moth.

Preferred Foodplant Oak

Accepted Alternate Foodplants Birch, Maple, Chestnut, Willow, and many other deciduous trees and shrubs

Diapause Cocoon

Ova Large, round, flattened cushion shape, with dark brown rings around the perimeter.

Larvae Typical of most larvae of the *Antheraea* group, and, in fact, an early name of this species was *Antheraea polyphemus*. Sedentary, solitary feeder and phlegmatic of disposition, they attain nearly four inches in length, and are proportionately fat. Pale green, sparsely covered with long hairs. Not urticating.

Rearing Requirements If you keep the cage or sleeve clean of frass, supply copious quantities of fresh food, and keep the brood under light airy conditions, you should have no trouble carrying them all to maturity. In the warmer southern regions, *polyphemus* is double brooded. Northern specimens make but a single brood each season. This species is prone to diseases if crowded too much or if not kept clean. Care should also be taken to make the cage or sleeve parasite and predator proof, because *polyphemus* is the natural prey of many of our common predators.

Cocoon *Polyphemus* spins up an egg-shaped cocoon which it hardens by saturation from within. No valve is present, and the peduncle is weak, allowing the cocoon to fall when the leaves come off the trees.

Adult This is one of our most beautiful moths. The light brown wings have a dusting of gray on the costal margin and pink tracery running vertically across the forewings. The hindwings are decorated with hyaline eyespots outlined in yellow, in a field of dark blue shading to black. There are smaller eyespots on the forewings. The span of an average male is nearly five inches. The male antennae are very large and feathery. Mating is easy in a roomy cage, and the mating continues through the entire day.

Tropea luna Cocoon. The cocoon of *luna* is usua[
spun up among the leaves at the base of the fo[
tree

Tropea luna These caterpillars greatly resemble those
of the genus *Antheraea*. They are just a little smaller

Tropea luna Ova

Tropea luna Mounted adult male

TROPEA (ACTIAS) LUNA

Family Saturniidae

Popular Name Luna Moth—Moon Moth

Range From Canada to Central America

Availability Generally available each season, since this is a very popular specimen.

Preferred Foodplant Hickory

Accepted Alternate Foodplants Walnut, Chestnut, Pecan, possibly Willow and Gum, Persimmon, and others of the Ebony family

Diapause Cocoon; sometimes double-brooded

Ova Medium large, round, very dark to black, and with a rough-appearing surface. Laid in irregular bunches.

Larvae Flesh translucent pale green with no really distinguishing markings other than a pale line running around the lateral just below the line of spiracles, which, in turn, are small and inconspicuous.

Rearing Requirements *Luna* does not require a specific environment although it thrives best in a light and airy cage or large sleeve. It does, however, require fresh food, and—since most members of the Hickory group wilt rather rapidly when cut—the breeder will have the greatest success rearing *luna* either in sleeves or cages on living foodplants. Because most of the food trees accepted by *luna* are large, with sparse foliage on widely spaced branches, sleeves are a better device than cages. The caterpillars will almost invariably spin their cocoon in a fold of the sleeve material, and—since they are delicate—considerable care must be taken to avoid tearing them apart when you peel them out of the material.

Cocoon Light, thin, papery. Sealed without a valve, and the pupa is loose within. If cocoons are damaged, the *luna* will emerge without crippling if it is removed from the broken cocoon and stored within a paper sleeve made of soft paper towel or napkin. Normally, the cocoon is spun among the fallen leaves of the food tree and allowed to remain on the ground under cover of the dead leaves.

Adult The Luna Moth seems to have been a favorite for many years. Certainly it is a lovely and delicate creature, and one to be desired in any collection. In common with all of the *Tropea* group, this moth will fade very badly after mounting if it is subjected even to weak light. The mount is best kept tightly covered and opened only for viewing. The overall color is a delicate pastel green with a deep maroon costa. The small clear eyespot on each forewing has a "stem" of maroon attaching the eye to the costal line. The eye on the hindwings is also clear, and surrounded by a darker area. The hindwings have long, delicate "tails" having a suggestion of maroon on their outer edges. About a five-inch span.

Brahmaea japonica Fifth instar larva

Brahmaea japonica Mounted adult male

BRAHMAEA JAPONICA

Family   Brahmaeidae

Popular Name   None to my knowledge

Range   Japan and the Indo-Asian Region

Availability   More readily obtainable then *Brahmaea wallichii;* most European or British dealers sell this species every season.

Preferred Foodplant   Lilac

Accepted Alternate Foodplants   Privet and possibly Cherry, Ash

Diapause   Pupa

Ova   Round, bun-shaped, tan to brown. Medium sized.

Larvae   In the early instars, this caterpillar is horned much like that of *wallichii*. In the final instar, the body is pale green with broken diagonal patches on each segment at the spiracle line. Just before the animal is ready to go underground to pupate, the dorsal area turns a deep, rich, red-chestnut color, and the line of the heart is very clearly defined. One can see the blood pulsing from end to end of the caterpillar.

Rearing Requirements   Spacious quarters, warmth, humid air, and plenty of fresh succulent leaves. A deep soil bed to dig into when pupating. If a pupating box is used it must be at least eight to ten inches deep.

Cocoon   A naked pupa, large, fat, shiny black-brown. A rather pronounced set of spines on the end with which the quite active pupa turns itself around and around in the burrow.

Adult   Almost exactly the same as *Brahmaea wallichii*, except smaller in size. The base color is cream; the wings are covered with all sorts of cryptic lines, spots, and mottlings in rich brown.

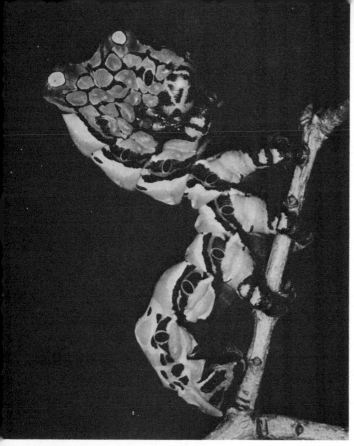

Brahmaea wallichii Pupa

Brahmaea wallichii Fifth instar larva in defensive posture on twig

Brahmaea wallichii Ova

Brahmaea wallichii Mounted adult female

BRAHMAEA WALLICHII

Family   Brahmaeidae

Popular Name   None to my knowledge

Range   Japan to India

Availability   In the past three or four years this species had been available from European breeders. Mr. Downey has also offered stock in this country.

Preferred Foodplant   Lilac

Accepted Alternate Foodplants   Privet and possibly Willow or Cherry. However, excellent results are obtained with Lilac and—since this plant is almost universally available—I should recommend it as the specific food.

Diapause   Pupa

Ova   Very large, round, bun-like. Flat on the bottom, with a slight concavity on the under side. There is also a very slight depression on the top, in the center of which is the dark micropyle. The color is like bread crust.

Larvae   A very striking and bizarre creature indeed. Looks like a miniature dragon when drawn up into its defensive posture. In the early instars, there are long, wavy black feelers—four on the first three segments and one on the last segment. In the fifth instar, these processes are discarded and in their place is a pale blue pearly spot. The body is white with orange-yellow dorsal and lateral patches separated by black patches extending diagonally rearward on each segment. The lateral surfaces of the first three segments are covered with scale-like patches greenish in color and outlined in black. On the dorsal surface between the first and second and the second and third segments are two large oval black spots. When the caterpillar is disturbed it tightly curls up the first three segments and rears the entire fore part of the body off the twig, presenting a formidable view of huge staring eyes (the black dorsal patches) from a head-on view, or a snaky animal with blue eyes (the "feeler" spots) from a lateral view.

Rearing Requirements   Large cage or sleeve. Much fresh food, and the leaves must be succulent. Warmth and humidity. Wrapping the cage in plastic, as for *Attacus edwardsi*, works well. I have found that the species of lilac with white flowers has much larger and juicier leaves than the common purple varieties. However, the larvae will feed on any species.

Cocoon   *Wallichii* makes a very large, glossy pupa deep underground, and wherever possible should be allowed to go down inside the cage where the larvae are reared, remaining underground throughout the winter with a heavy mulch of peatmoss over the surface of the earth. Remember that this is one of the very first species to emerge in the spring; the cage should either be left in place through the winter or erected over the shrub well before all the snow is gone and the spring thaws begin.

Adult   A marvelous example of cryptic coloration, this moth is a study in brown. The base color of the wings is a dark cream, and the wings are covered with wavy lines, bars, dots, and patches of dark warm brown. There are two ocelli on the bottom center portion of the forewings. The body is comparatively small and has a luxuriant cape of brown fur.

Arctia caja Cocoon in leaf wrappings

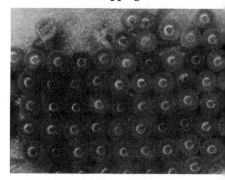

Arctia caja Fifth instar larva has a magnificent covering of silver-tipped hair

Arctia caja Ova. Laid in neat patch. Some of the embryos can be seen throu the shells

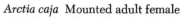

Arctia caja Mounted adult female

ARCTIA CAJA

Family   Arctiidae

Popular Name   Garden Tiger, Tiger Moth

Range   Almost worldwide

Availability   Usually readily available from most breeders.

Preferred Foodplant   Dandelion

Accepted Alternate Foodplants   Plantain and other broad-leaved weed plants

Diapause   Hibernates as a partly-grown caterpillar

Ova   Very small, yellowish, translucent, laid in broad sheet-like patches.

Larvae   Very beautiful in the fifth instar, with a luxuriant coat of long silvery-white hair. They very strongly resemble silver fox fur. The bodies are dark red-brown and show through the cape of hair. They have the habit of curling up and dropping off the foodplant when disturbed, common with most *Arctiids*.

Rearing Requirements   *Caja* will live under conditions that will quickly kill many other species, which is not to say that you should rear them so. They will accept food whether it is crisp or wilted, and this tends to make the breeder a bit careless. Actually, they thrive much better on fresh food.

It is somewhat of a nuisance to rear hibernating caterpillars, but the work may be easier if you use a bottomless cage set outside and liberally supplied with rocks under which the larvae can find shelter. Dandelion or plantain plants can be transplanted into the cage; when transplanting, be sure to get deep down to the tap root, or the plant will not survive. When the cold weather sets in, the larvae will go into their dormant stage. In their early instars, the caterpillars hibernate among the roots of their foodplants, under rocks or in sheltered crevices. At times, during a prolonged warm spell, they might emerge from their hibernation to nibble at a leaf or two, returning to their diapause until late spring, when they come out, feed up, and spin their cocoon in a sheltered spot.

Cocoon   A flimsy cocoon is spun of weak silk among the old leaves or just under the surface of moss or around the roots of the foodplant. The pupa is small, shiny, very dark red-brown.

Adult   The adult emerges in the early summer, to mate and deposit her ova. The males and females are hard to distinguish except for the antennae. Both are brightly colored, cream ground with large uneven blotches of brown covering the forewings. Red-orange ground covered with metallic black spots on the hindwings. About one-and-one-half- to two-inch span.

Estigmene acraea Mounted adult female

Estigmene acraea Cocoon and exposed pupa

Estigmene acraea Fifth instar larva

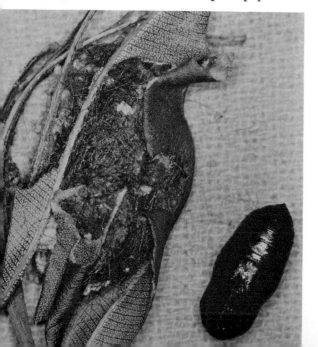

ESTIGMENE ACRAEA

Family Arctiidae

Popular Name Saltmarsh Caterpillar

Range Most of the United States

Availability The only dealer that has offered eggs of this species to my knowledge is Mr. Duke Downey, of Sheridan, Wyoming. The caterpillars are easy to collect in the wild, however.

Preferred Foodplant Oleander, Sea Grape, Dandelion, Dock, Plantain

Accepted Alternate Foodplants Almost omniverous. It will probably thrive on whatever you care to offer it.

Diapause Caterpillar

Ova Small, pale, whitish, indented, round.

Larvae The body is cream color speckled with purplish dots, and with a broad band of blue-black on the dorsal surface. Encircling each segment is a row of rounded tubercules, from each of which springs a tuft of short stiff hairs—brown on the lateral surfaces and black on the dorsal. The last three segments carry a brush of long white hairs growing from the dorsal tubercules.

Rearing Requirements Nothing special is necessary to successfully rear this species except to keep them confined and supply them with enough food. They seem to have no preference as to diet, and will readily accept almost anything offered in their later instars. The young larvae, however, tend to be finicky as to acceptance, and seem to prefer to start feeding on whatever foodplants were used to rear their parent stock. This will vary according to the locality from which the breeding stock was obtained. In Florida, for instance, *acraea* feeds avidly on either Sea Grape or Oleander, while in the northwestern section of the country the preferred food is dandelion and plantain.

Cocoon The cocoon is spun up in a leaf of the foodplant, and is made of coarse brown silk, interwoven with hairs from the body of the caterpillar. The pupa within is short, stout, and shiny black. The tail is blunt and rounded, rather than tapered. The wing cases and the abdominal segments are very poorly defined.

Adult This is a very pretty moth. The sexes differ in coloring. Both have white forewings, speckled with black. The same color persists on the hindwings of the female, but those of the male are bright orange-yellow with a few dark spots. The bodies of both are similar. The thoracic section carries a cape of white fur. The abdomen is deep yellow with a row of black dorsal spots. Two-inch span or a little larger.

Isia isabella Cocoons are spun up under protec
rocks, bark, etc.

Isia isabella Ova. Tiny, chalk-white laid in ind
criminate patches

Isia isabella Mature larva in heart of foodplant just
before hibernation

Isia isabella Mounted adult female

ISIA ISABELLA

Family   Arctiidae

Popular Name   Woolly Bear

Range   All over the United States and up into Canada

Availability   Not generally available in dealer's stocks. Look for the caterpillars crossing almost any country road in the early fall, and again in the early spring.

Preferred Foodplant   Plantain

Accepted Alternate Foodplants   Dandelion, a great variety of low-growing weeds, many grasses

Diapause   Caterpillar

Ova   Pale yellow, small, round, translucent, laid in patches.

Larvae   Hardly anything need be said about this familiar animal. What boy has not taken the woolly bear from the road in the fall, to watch it curl up in a circle immediately when it is disturbed? Red-brown in the center, jet black at both ends, the animal looks as though it is covered in plush.

Rearing Requirements   As with all the arctids, a place must be provided for the caterpillars to hibernate in the fall, and where they will be kept cold through the winter, but will not freeze. On warm days, they break hibernation to nibble a plant or two, and return to their sanctuary as the afternoon starts to cool.

Cocoon   *Isabella* makes a brown woolly cocoon out of rough silk and the hairs from its body; the cocoon is secreted in crevices, under stones, or in sheltered places. The cocoon is small and soft. It is made in the late spring or early summer and the moth emerges soon thereafter to mate and lay eggs. The pupa is dark with a dull surface.

Adult   The females are a bit darker in color than the males. The forewings are ocherous yellow with a dark spot in the centers and very faint markings over the surfaces. The hindwings are pinkish-ochre with a few black specks on the margin. The color of the male is the same except it is tan on the wings and the hindwings lack the row of black specks. The bodies of both sexes are golden-tan with three rows of neat black spots on the abdominal segments. The thorax carries a cape of tan hairs. Wingspan about two inches.

Catocala concumbens Mounted adult female

Catocala concumbens The fancy little pillows of the *Catocalas* look like beautiful miniature hassocks. The eggs are so small that you need a strong glass to see the surface texture

Catocala concumbens Fifth instar larva

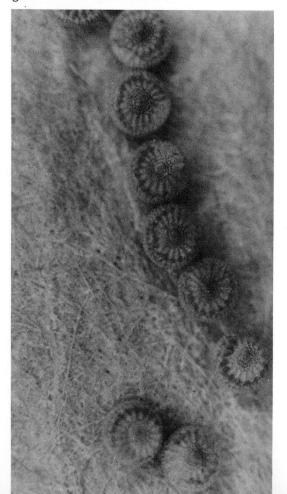

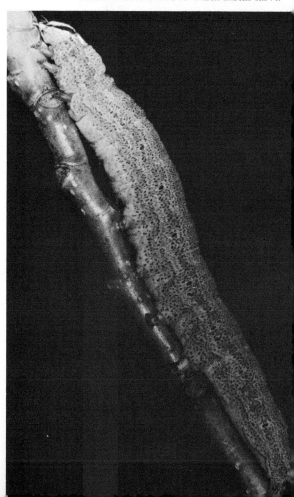

Family   Noctuidae

Popular Name   According to Holland, this moth is called the Sleepy Underwing. I hesitate to perpetuate the continuance of the ridiculous names assigned to this genus in his book, which had better be left to die a natural death.

Range   Most of the United States eastern seaboard from New Jersey north to Canada

Availability   While this species is not always available, one or another of the *Catocalas* are; the larvae are so similar that any one of them will do for rearing purposes.

Preferred Foodplant   Willow

Accepted Alternate Foodplants   Poplar may be accepted

Diapause   Ova

Ova   The ova of this species are practically identical with those of most of the other members of the genus. Round, flattened cushions, sharply ridged vertically, with a slight ring around the periphery.

Larvae   To describe one *Catocala* is to describe the genus. They are unbelievably lively when they emerge from the egg. Thread-like and tiny, they gallop all over the hatching box, and are expert at escaping from the smallest aperture. *Catocala* caterpillars do not develop their prolegs until their later instars, and the young larvae move like an inchworm, in rapid loopings of the body. In the final instar the prolegs are developed and the animal hugs the branches of the foodplant. The ventral surface generally bears a row of round black spots on a reddish ground.

Rearing Requirements   The cage or sleeve must be very tight to keep these specimens from escaping. They are night feeders, and should not be disturbed during the daylight hours.

Cocoon   Some of the species spin a flimsy cocoon of sorts, others go slightly underground or under fallen leaves or into a crack in the bark of the food tree. The pupa is dark and medium in size. Shortly after forming up, the pupa becomes coated with a bluish-white dust.

Adult   The adults are very similar, with the forewings very cryptically colored in bars, streaks, and mottlings of gray, and the hindwings red with black circular bands. The color does not show until the moth flies. Some species have blue, orange, or white hindwings.

Catocala fraxini Mounted adult female

Catocala fraxini These interesting caterpillars are so like the twigs they rest upon, even to the leaf scars, that they are virtually invisible

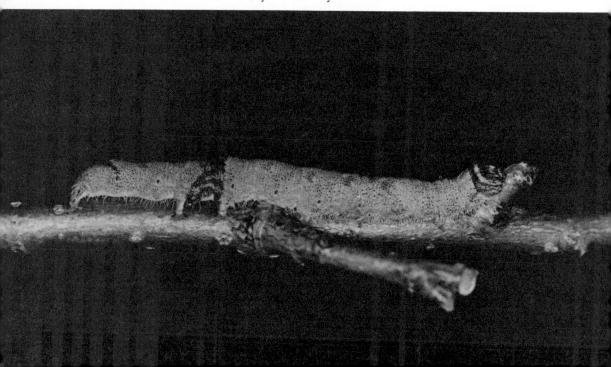

CATOCALA FRAXINI

Family Noctuidae

Popular Name Blue Underwing

Range Europe and the Indo-Asian Area

Availability European dealers always offer this popular underwing in season. A few domestic breeders sometimes have eggs in the fall.

Preferred Foodplant Willow

Accepted Alternate Foodplants Poplar, Sallow

Diapause Egg

Ova Small, flattened, round eggs, beautifully ridged and dimpled. Very pale tan color.

Larvae Like all the larvae of the *Catocala* moths, this one is a master at concealment, resembling as it does a twig with a leaf scar. Gray peppered with black. The leaf scar well defined. It has a short fringe of stiff hairs along the lower laterals which, when the caterpillar is in repose, hug the twig upon which the animal rests, blending in so well with the twig that the caterpillar is all but invisible. Belly reddish with several graduated round black spots.

Rearing Requirements Nothing special. They will do as well on cut food as on living trees. This is a night-feeding species, remaining at rest and hidden along the stems of the foodplant during the day. If you are rearing them on cut food, put the fresh leaves in the cage during the late evening rather than during the day. These caterpillars can escape through very small openings because of the small size of the heads. They can tolerate somewhat crowded quarters, and when dormant congregate in twos and threes together in the stems.

Cocoon The cocoon is made just underground, and is a flimsy affair, housing a short, very dark red-brown pupa. After forming up the pupa becomes coated with a blue-white dust, in common with most *Catocala* pupae. The tails are sharp and the pupa smooth and sharply tapered.

Adult This is one of the handsomest of the underwings. It is also one of the largest. The forewings are gray with red-black markings and a well-defined white spot in the center of each wing. The hindwings are dark black-brown bordered in white with a blue band dividing the wing area into thirds. Span up to three inches or more.

Catocala nupta Mounted adult male

Catocala nupta The eggs of most *Catocalas* are very beautifully textured

Catocala nupta Fifth instar larva. They closely resemble the twigs they rest upon most of the day

CATOCALA NUPTA

Family   Noctuidae

Popular Name   Red Underwing

Range   Europe generally, on into Indo-Asian Region

Availability   European breeders always offer eggs or pupae of this species in the fall.

Preferred Foodplant   Willow

Accepted Alternate Foodplants   Poplar and Sallow

Diapause   Egg

Ova   Round, flattened, beautifully ridged. Pale creamy-tan in color.

Larvae   *Catocala* caterpillars are often mistaken for those of the "Inchworm" group (Geometers) because the prolegs are far to the rear of the bodies and the animal has to hump itself along the branch. When the tiny larvae hatch they almost explode out of the egg. Tiny, and thread-like, they immediately gallop all over the container, with astonishing speed. This one is, like most underwing larvae, flattened with hairy protuberances along the sides which blend into the branch upon which the larva rests during the daytime. A night feeder, food, if cut branches, should be offered in the evening so it will be fresh during feeding activity.

Watch out for escapees. They are so tiny when hatched, and so very active, that ordinary screening offers no barrier at all—they will pass through the fine mesh at a run. A plastic sandwich box is best until they attain some size.

Rearing Requirements   Nothing special, except to see that their quarters are escape proof and that the animals have an abundance of fresh food. Do as well on cut food as on living trees. They can stand somewhat crowded quarters, which is to say that a large brood may be reared in a single large cage, rather than splitting it up among several containers.

Cocoon   *Nupta* spins a silken cocoon among the leaves of the foodplant or under loose bark. The pupa is long and tapered, and is generally held in a curved position rather than straight as in the case of other moths. The pupa is heavily covered with a blue-white dust.

Adult   This is a handsome underwing, with the forewings in shades of dark gray with obscure wavy markings strongly resembling bark. When the hindwings are exposed they are very showy in very dark rich red with a wavy black band, and a thin white edging. Span about two inches or more.

Euparthenos nubilis Mounted adult female

Euparthenos nubilis Fifth instar larva on Golden Locust

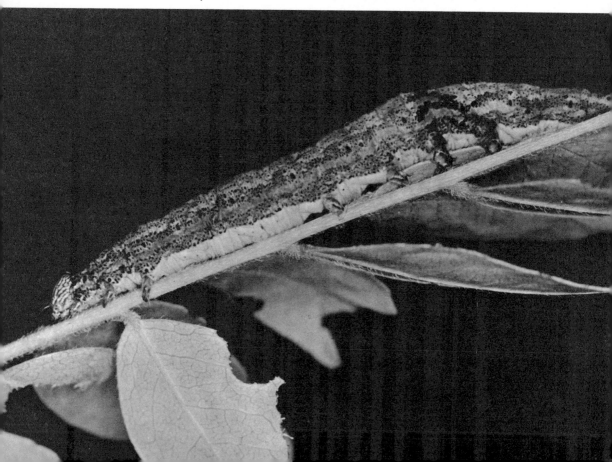

EUPARTHENOS NUBILIS

Family   Noctuidae

Popular Name   None to my knowledge

Range   North Atlantic States to Arizona

Availability   Not often offered by American breeders. The caterpillars are some-times plentiful in the wild on Locust, and gravid females will come to black lights.

Preferred Foodplant   Locust

Accepted Alternate Foodplants   None to my knowledge, although it has been reported that the species will accept Willow

Diapause Pupa

Ova   Small, pale, round, slightly compressed.

Larvae   The species greatly resembles the *Catocala* caterpillers. It has the same flattened structure, with a fringe hugging the branch stem of the foodplant and blending in to become invisible unless it moves. Nocturnal feeder. The upper portion of the body is pinkish, covered with dark specks, and a pink line runs under the spiracles. The "leaf scar" is well defined and striped with dark brown. The belly is white, and slightly convex rather than concave as in the larvae of the *Catocalas.*

Rearing Requirements   Does not take well to cut food, since Locust does not hold up well when brought indoors. The caterpillars are escape artists and the cage in which they are reared must be tightly constructed.

Cocoon   *Nubilis* makes a flimsy cocoon of a few layers of silk either just under the surface of the rubble on the ground, or among fallen leaves. The pupa within greatly resembles those of the various *Catocalas.*

Adult   Looks exactly like a *Catocala* moth. The forewings are gray with cryptic wavy lines and markings. The hindwings are orange with three irregular black bands traversing them. The lower two bands are so positioned as to cause the orange ground to appear to be a row of round dots on a black ground. There is a black crescent facing outwards near the upper edge of each hindwing. Span nearly three inches.

Panthea coenobita Mounted adult male

Panthea coenobita Cocoon and exposed pupa

Panthea coenobita Fifth instar larva

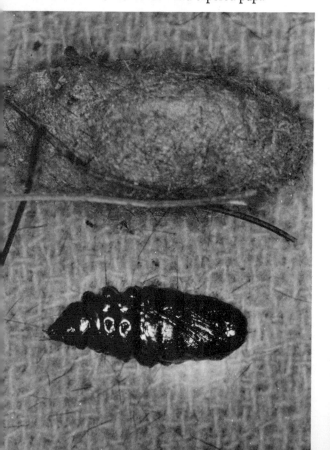

PANTHEA COENOBITA

Family   Noctuidae

Popular Name   Pine Arches

Range   Europe

Availability   Generally always available from European breeders

Preferred Foodplant   Pine

Accepted Alternate Foodplants   None

Diapause   Cocoon

Ova   Small, seedlike, grayish, round.

Larvae   Much like the caterpillars of the *Lasiocampidae,* this species is flattened and hirsute. Long "guard hairs" stand out from the fuzzy body. The head is covered with small freckles, and there is a white arch marking below each spiracle.

Rearing Requirements   This is a very easy caterpillar to rear. Keep it supplied with fresh pine, and it will thrive. Since it is a small caterpillar, and a sedentary one, a small cage will do nicely to rear them in. It should be well ventilated, however.

Cocoon   The caterpillar spins a somewhat loose silken cocoon among the needles of the foodplant. There is no valve, but one end of the cocoon is more pointed than the other, suggesting a place of exit. The pupa is very dark and quite shiny, with the abdominal segments very deeply indented.

Adult   The moth is small—not over an inch and a quarter in wingspan. The ground color of the forewings is white, completely covered with dark gray cryptic markings. The hindwings are silvery gray. A beautiful little creature.

Pyrophila pyramidoides Mounted adult male

Pyrophila pyramidoides Ova. Most of these are infertile and are beginning to collapse

Pyrophila pyramidoides Fifth instar larva on wil grape

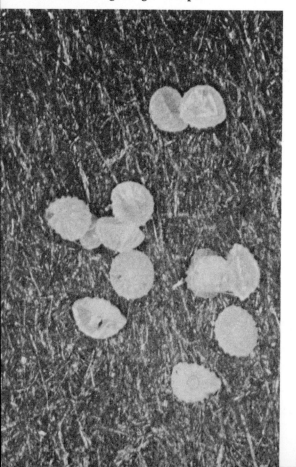

PYROPHILA PYRAMIDOIDES

Family   Noctuidae

Popular Name   Copper Underwing

Range   From the East Coast west to Colorado

Availability   Not often available. Mr. Duke Downey of Sheridan, Wyoming, offers eggs now and then. This species can be taken in the larval stage from the foodplant in the wild, and gravid females taken at lights.

Preferred Foodplant   Grape

Accepted Alternate Foodplants   Rhododendron, Virginia Creeper, and many other shrubs and herbaceous plants

Diapause   Egg

Ova   Very small, round, and yellow in color.

Larvae   This is a small caterpillar, but a pretty one. The final instar has a blue-green body peppered with yellow to orange spots. There is an orange line running down the middle of the lateral surfaces, darker on the thoracic segments. The spiracles are blue and centered on this orange line.

Rearing Requirements   Nothing special. This is an easy species to rear, and it feeds rapidly, making its pupa in the late summer, emerging to deposit the overwintering eggs. The caterpillar does not go far underground, preferring to make its thin cocoon among rubbish just at the surface.

Cocoon   Thin and flimsy. The pupa is small and very dark. Smooth surface with a very sharp tail. Made among surface rubbish.

Adult   A small moth, not over two inches in span. The forewings are dark brown-gray covered with cryptic markings very like the wings of *Catocala*. The hindwings are bright copper in color with a darker shading toward the upper outer edge. The body is dark brown-gray with five light bands marking the segments of the abdomen.

Apatelodes torrefacta Mounted adult male

Apatelodes torrefacta The pupa of this species is
polished so highly that it appears to be lacquered

Apatelodes torrefacta Fifth instar larva
PHOTO BY PAUL E. STONE, MUNITH, MICHIGAN

APATELODES TORREFACTA

Family   Notodontidae

Popular Name   None

Range   From the Mississippi River, east to the Atlantic, and from Canada to the Gulf of Mexico

Availability   Not generally available, although the larvae can be collected wild without too much difficulty, or gravid females taken at dark lights.

Preferred Foodplant   Cherry

Accepted Alternate Foodplants   Possibly Willow—none other known to me

Diapause   Subterranean pupa

Ova   Very small, yellow, round. Laid in patches.

Larvae   Like a puff of snow-white fur. The caterpillar is about an inch and one-half long; the body is white, completely covered with long white fur. In the last instar there are several broken stripes of black on each segment and the hairs are slightly shorter.

Rearing Requirements   Nothing at all special. The larvae are sedentary and quiet. They do not eat a great deal, but like the food to be fresh.

Cocoon   The caterpillar makes its pupa underground. The pupa is shiny and almost black. The joints between the segments are granulated and the tail spike is very short and stubby.

Adult   Like a great many of the *Notodonts* the moth is small—about one and one-half inches across the wings—and steel gray in color. A black cape extends across the body into the rear edge of the forewings, and a few dark lines run at right angles to the costa into the forewings. The outer ends of the forewings are indented. The hindwings are plain gray with a small dark patchy line on the inner edges.

177

Cerura scitiscripta Mounted adult male

Cerura scitiscripta This cocoon was made on the rubber cork of the brooder. The cocoon is made of chewed rubber

Cerura scitiscripta Fifth instar larva on a poplar

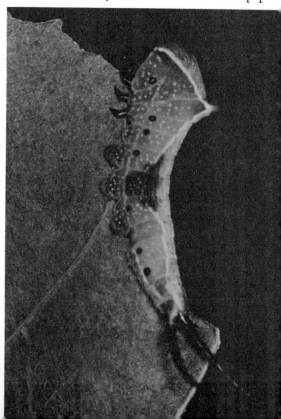

CERURA SCITISCRIPTA

Family   Notodontidae

Popular Name   I know of no popular name for this species, although I suppose it could be called the Puss Moth, the same as the British *Cerura vinula,* of which this one is a miniature version.

Range   Throughout the United States into Mexico

Availability   Not often found in dealers' stocks, this moth is better collected as young larvae in the wild.

Preferred Foodplant   Poplar

Accepted Alternate Foodplants   Willow, Lime (*Tilia*)

Diapause   Cocoon

Ova   Extremely small, dark, bun-shaped, with a minute depression at the micropyle.

Larvae   Almost exactly the same as the Puss Moth of Great Britain. Black when first hatched, with "ears" and a tail held stiffly upright. The tail is really a modification of the rear claspers. In the later instars the body is green with a pale blue wash covering the dorsal area. A brown saddle colors the sides directly over the second pair of prolegs. There is a curious bump on the third thoracic segment making a sort of process or tubercule. The bifurcated tail contains pink whiplike threads that are extruded at the slightest provocation, and which exude a strong odor. The fully grown caterpillar is not much more than one inch in length.

Rearing Requirements   To collect the larvae in the wild is fairly easy, if you have access to poplar groves. Look in the early spring on the leaves of young poplar saplings. The tiny caterpillars stand out starkly because of their velvety black color against the bright dusty green of the leaves. Sometimes several can be found on one tree. Nothing special is required for this species, except, as in the case with *C. vinula,* they must be supplied with large twigs or a piece of wood to use in fabricating their hard box-like cocoons. As with *vinula,* also, the chance of the pupa successfully emerging is greatly depleted if the cocoon is opened to expose the pupa within. In one lot of *scitiscripta* being reared in an indoor brooder, the caterpillars became ready to pupate during a period when I was away for a couple of days. Lacking the wood for their cocoon, one of them actually chewed a depression in the rubber cork supporting the foodplant twigs and made its cocoon out of the chewed rubber particles!

Cocoon   This species utilizes part of the support in making its cocoon, the same way that *Cerura vinula* does. A small hollow is chewed out of the bark of a branch of the foodplant, and the chewed matter used to erect the top half of the cocoon. When completed, the cocoon is hard and impervious, and the pupa within is loose and will rattle around. The moth will almost never survive if the cocoon is cut open to expose the pupa. A small hole is cut in the end of the cocoon when the adult emerges, through which it pulls itself to expand its wings.

Adult   A small moth, wingspan about one and a quarter inches. It has plain gray hindwings, white forewings covered with delicate tracery of gray. The body is white with gray stripes across the segmental joints. The antennae are plumed and very delicately feathered. A very pretty specimen and one that is not nearly enough appreciated.

Cerura vinula Mounted adult female

Cerura vinula Cocoons on board

Cerura vinula Fifth instar larva

CERURA VINULA

Family   Notodontidae

Popular Name   Puss Moth

Range   British Isles and continental Europe

Availability   Always available from European breeders, especially those in England where this is a very popular insect.

Preferred Foodplant   Poplar

Accepted Alternate Foodplants   Willow, Sallow

Diapause   Cocoon

Ova   Very interesting, bun-shaped, flat on the bottom and the top very slightly drawn up. The micropyle is dark, set in a slight depression on the top. Purple-chestnut color.

Larvae   The popular name was given to these curious little animals because of the remarkable resemblance of the newly-hatched caterpillars to tiny black kittens! The claspers have been modified into two long streamers which are held stiffly erect at the rear, and from which can be protruded pink osmeteria which give off a strong odor which is probably offensive to predators. At hatching, the body is completely black, velvety in appearance with two "ears" at the head. Looks exactly like a kitten with its tail held erect. In the final instar the caterpillar is yellow-green with a diamond-shaped saddle of purple. The head and the first segment are purple and the insect has the habit of pulling its head back into the first couple of segments, presenting a square purplish frontal aspect.

Rearing Requirements   There is nothing special about the rearing requirements of *vinula*, except they prefer fresh leaves, as, for that matter, do most all caterpillars regardless of the species.

Cocoon   For the caterpillar to pupate, the breeder must supply them with wood of some sort. Either short sections of the trunks of the foodplant trees, softwood boards, or perhaps a piece of shingle. The caterpillar chews out an elliptical hollow, using the chewed wood pulp to build a roof over the cavity like the lid of a box. The pulp hardens into a cover nearly as impenetrable as the wood itself. Inside this chamber the pupa is formed, and, after pupation, one can rattle the pupa inside the cocoon like a pea in a whistle. Not that it is good practice to do so, however, since severe vibration may cause the pupa to fail to emerge. It has been my experience that if the cocoon is opened and the pupa removed, it will die without emerging as an adult. Quite evidently the moth must chew its way out of the cocoon in order to complete its life cycle. At any rate, I have never had an opened cocoon reach maturity.

Adult   The adult is very pretty. White wings and body, with black veining and tracery covering them. The abdominal segments of the body are darker gray, and there is a thick cape over the thoracic section. About two-inch wingspan.

Notodonta ziczac Mounted adult female

Notodonta ziczac Fifth instar larva in typical pose

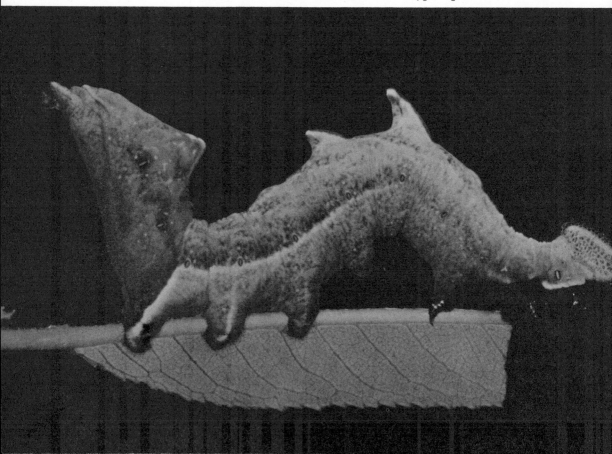

NOTODONTA ZICZAC

Family Notodontidae

Popular Name Pebble Prominent

Range Europe, British Isles, to Armenia and Amurland

Availability Always available from European dealers. Seldom offered in the United States.

Preferred Foodplant Willow

Accepted Alternate Foodplants Sallow and Poplar

Diapause Subterranean pupa

Ova Small, shaped like a flattened bun. Pale colored.

Larvae A real weird creature. Body a sort of pinkish brown-gray, peppered with minute speckles. Naked, with two fleshy spines on the dorsal surface. Beginning at the rear of the last pair of prolegs, the body is deep orange-red. The rear section of the animal is kept elevated in the air most of the time, giving the caterpillar a wavy shape.

Rearing Requirements Needs fresh leaves, and seems to languish in indoor cages unless the leaves are very succulent. Since the caterpillar is a small one, it can escape through small openings. However, it does not seem to want to wander about too much. Likes it cool and airy.

Cocoon The caterpillar pupates in a cocoon of earth made just under the surface of the ground. Since it is normally double-brooded, it is the late brood that overwinters in the cocoon. There have been three broods in captivity, but this is not usual.

Adult A small moth, but nicely marked. The forewings are brown with darker cryptic markings and a white patch near the center at the costal margin. The hindwings are cream to white with a dark thin emargination.

Phalera bucephala Mounted adult female

Phalera bucephala Ova

Phalera bucephala Bright orange is the dominant color of this bristly caterpillar

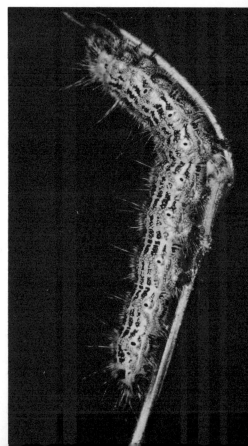

PHALERA BUCEPHALA

Family   Notodontidae

Popular Name   Buff Tip (In Europe)

Range   British Isles and continental Europe

Availability   Most European breeders offer ova each season.

Preferred Foodplant   Oak

Accepted Alternate Foodplants   Hazel, Lime (*Tilia*), Elm, among many others

Diapause   Pupa

Ova   Shaped like a rounded button; half white with a black spot in the center, grayish black on the bottom. Small. Laid in small batches on the undersides of leaves.

Larvae   The name *bucephala* gives a clue to the appearance of the newly hatched larvae. From the Greek, Bucephalus was the celebrated war-horse of Alexander the Great, and was supposed to have had a large ox-like head. Truly the heads—in proportion to the bodies of the first instar larvae—are enormous! In the final instar the caterpillar is yellow with broken black lines. They are very gregarious.

Rearing Requirements   There seems to be no special rearing requirements for this species except plenty of food—almost any kind. They are not specific in their diet and will take a great many trees.

Cocoon   The caterpillar does not burrow very deeply into the ground to pupate, and prefers soft earth to hard soil. The pupating box is ideal for these larvae.

Adult   It is from the adult that the popular name tagged onto this moth is derived. The wings are light gray, with a large buff patch at the outer ends of the forewings. The hindwings are cream to white. Span about one and three-quarters to two inches.

Anisota senatoria Mounted adult female   PHOTO BY RAYMOND OSLAND, ENGLAND

Anisota senatoria The pupa of this species is rough and has skirted segments

Anisota senatoria Fifth instar larva
PHOTO BY PAUL E. STONE, MUNITH, MICHIGAN

ANISOTA SENATORIA

Family   Ceratocampidae

Popular Name   I do not know of a popular name

Range   The Atlantic States into Canada

Availability   This moth is often available, in the form of eggs, from Duke Downey in Sheridan, Wyoming; but breeders in general do not handle it because it is not one of the striking, dramatic moths of our country.

Preferred Foodplant   Oak

Accepted Alternate Foodplants   None to my knowledge

Diapause   Subterranean pupa

Ova   Small, rounded, pale-colored. Laid on twigs of the food plant.

Larvae   Smooth, black body with orange dorsal and lateral stripes running the entire length of the animal. The segments are studded with very short stiff spines, sparsely located. A couple of longer spines adorn the second segment. The head is black.

Rearing Requirements   Nothing special. This caterpillar will accept cut food as well as fresh, provided the leaves are not wilted. It can be reared in small quarters, which is not to say that you should deliberately stuff a large brood into a small container.

Cocoon   Dark brown-black. The surface is dull and rough. The caterpillar does not make a cocoon worthy of the name, but pupates underground in a shallow depression. The segments are well defined, and the surface of the pupa turns up into a little ridge at each joint. The tail spike is long and sharp.

Adult   Wingspan about two to two and one-half inches. The wings are slightly translucent, pale tan in color. The hindwings are perfectly plain. The forewings are dusted with irregular chestnut spots or freckles, and have a small round hyaline spot near the center. A dark dusty line separates the outer third of the forewings. The body is plain tan and is quite large for the size of the moth.

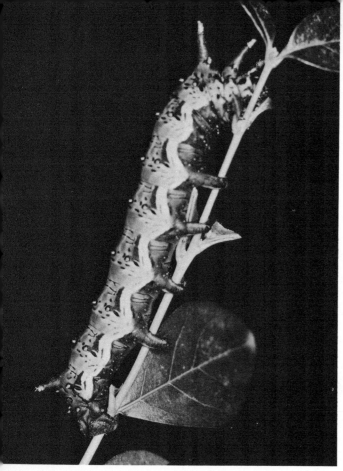

Citheronia brissottii Pupae

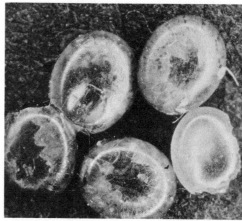

Citheronia brissottii Fifth instar larva

Citheronia brissottii Ova, showing the embryos within the shells. One egg has hatched and another has just broken through

Citheronia brissottii Mounted adult female

CITHERONIA BRISSOTTII

Family   Ceratocampidae

Popular Name   Spiny Worm, Spine Devil (in South America)

Range   Most of South America

Availability   Generally very rare and hard to find. Sometimes ova are offered, but not often. This is true of all the *Citheroniidae*.

Preferred Foodplant   Walnut

Accepted Alternate Foodplants   I know of none, but almost certainly this species will accept Hickory and Butternut, Pecan and related trees

Diapause   Subterranean pupa

Ova   Large, oval, yellow and milky-translucent.

Larvae   This is one of the truly fearsome-looking caterpillars. It is covered with branched and spined tubercules, and is as prickly as it looks. Severely urticating, it is best not to try to handle the caterpillar, since it attains a formidable size and is capable of imparting a bad sting.

Rearing Requirements   *Brissottii*, in common with others of the genus, require fresh leaves, warm and airy conditions, and plenty of room. As the larvae enter their fourth and fifth instars their appetite greatly increases, and, if you are cage-rearing them, you must take care to see that they are constantly supplied. As the time for pupation approaches, the caterpillars become very restless and start to wander about. A pupating box or other accommodation must now be supplied. This box must be at least ten inches deep, since the larvae go down for a considerable distance before settling down to pupate. If possible, the pupae should be left undisturbed in the ground or box over winter, otherwise they are liable to form up and emerge prematurely, with a resultant loss of breeding stock.

Cocoon   This species makes only a hollow underground, with a strand or two of silk. Nothing that would pass as a cocoon. The pupa is large and plump, with the abdominal segments sharply delineated.

Adult   Body is large, russet colored with a yellow band at each segment. Wings rusty gray-brown with the veins marked out in rust. Oval yellow patches occupy most of the cells between the veins. The female is quite a bit larger than the male, about three-and-one-half-inch span.

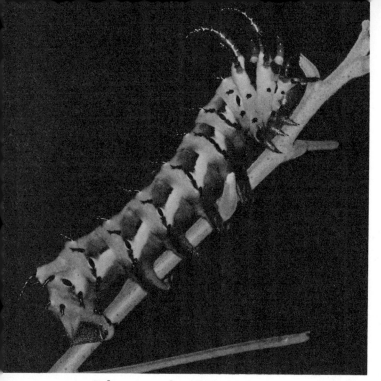

Citheronia regalis Pupa

Citheronia regalis Fifth instar larva

Citheronia regalis Ova

Citheronia regalis Mounted adult female

CITHERONIA REGALIS

Family   Ceratocampidae

Popular Name   Hickory Horned Devil

Range   Eastern United States

Availability   Like the others of this genus, *regalis* is generally hard to come by. Sometimes several seasons pass with no stock being offered.

Preferred Foodplant   Walnut

Accepted Alternate Foodplants   Hickory, Pecan, Butternut

Diapause   Subterranean pupa

Ova   Large, yellow, milky-translucent.

Larvae   Not one for a timid person to come upon suddenly. Looks like a small dragon, with long curving spiky horns projecting from the thoracic segments, and the rest of the body as fearfully covered with shorter protuberances. This is also one of the very severely urticating species, and should be handled with care. Often attains a length of seven inches.

Rearing Requirements   Large quantities of fresh food, light, airy surroundings, and plenty of warmth seem to be the most important needs of this caterpillar. An occasional sprinkle of tepid water on the leaves will not do any harm, and the larvae seem to enjoy it. If the larvae are being cage reared outdoors, a sheet of plastic wrapped around the sides of the cage will be of considerable value in keeping it warm within. This species seems to be rather susceptible to cold, and the feeding rate slows considerably as the temperature drops.

When the time for pupation arrives and the larvae become restless, a deep pupating box or otherwise confined and protected area outdoors should be supplied. If possible, let the pupa remain underground undisturbed through the winter.

Cocoon   The pupa of *regalis* is large, stout, and rough-surfaced. Blunt tip and short spine. Dusty red-brown in color.

Adult   This species is among the largest of the *Citheroniidae,* and the female attains a span of from five to six inches. The general overall color of the forewings is a pale grayed sepia with the veins lined in rust. The hindwings are rust color with large yellow patches at the juncture of the forewings. There are yellow spots sparsely scattered on the forewings.

Citheronia splendens Adult female

Citheronia splendens Pupa

Citheronia splendens Larva in the fifth instar. The broken line do[wn]
the center of the back is the heart

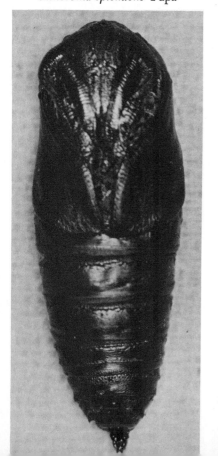

CITHERONIA SPLENDENS

Family   Ceratocampidae

Popular Name   None to my knowledge

Range   Mexico and Central America

Availability   Quite rare and very seldom available on the market. European breeders are more likely to offer ova or pupae than those in the United States.

Preferred Foodplant   Walnut

Accepted Alternate Foodplants   Hickory, Pecan, and Butternut

Diapause   Subterranean pupa

Ova   About the same as others of this group. Large, pale yellow and milky-translucent.

Larvae   Not so formidable in appearance as *Citheronia regalis* or *C. brissottii*, nor as large as these two species. The caterpillar is pale green-gray with small sparse tubercules bearing tiny spines. The larvae are urticating, but not nearly as severely as its relatives.

Rearing Requirements   The same as for all *Citheroniae*. Fresh food, warmth, roomy confines, and a sprinkle of tepid water now and then. When the caterpillar is ready to pupate, its skin becomes tightly stretched over its bloated body, and the heart is clearly visible—pulsating up and down the length of the animal; it also becomes very restless. It likes a deep box to pupate in. In common with its cousins, it will form up and emerge prematurely if not kept cold after pupation.

Cocoon   The pupa of *splendens* is almost impossible to distinguish between any of the other *Citheroniidae*. Short, very plump, dark brown-black. The wing cases are very well defined and the entire surface of the pupa is granular and dull.

Adult   The male has a span of about three inches. The wings are light charcoal gray with the veins prominently marked in rust. A row of oval yellow patches occupy each cell in a line about one third of the way in from the edge of the forewings. The hindwings are divided at about the middle with the upper solid yellow section bearing two gray spots, and the lower half matching the forewing coloration. The body is much redder than *regalis* or *brissottii*, and has the abdominal segments lined with yellow.

Dryocampa rubicunda Mounted adult male

Dryocampa rubicunda Fifth instar larva on Silver Maple

DRYOCAMPA (ANISOTA) RUBICUNDA

Family   Ceratocampidae

Popular Name   Rosy Maple Moth

Range   United States

Availability   Mr. Duke Downey of Sheridan, Wyoming, often offers eggs or larvae of this species. I have seldom seen them for sale by other breeders.

Preferred Foodplant   This moth is a specific feeder, favoring Silver Maple (*Acer saccharinum*)

Accepted Alternate Foodplants   Any of the other Maples

Diapause   Pupa

Ova   Small, rounded, pale when laid, darkening when near hatching time.

Larvae   Yellow body, axially striped, with dark lines. A row of dark dots lines the sides under the row of spiracles. The surface of the body is covered with minute spiky protuberances. Two long "horns" stand out from the second segment. A short stiff spine points rearward from each segment just above the proleg.

Rearing Requirements   This species likes an airy situation, and does not take too well to close confinement. Also, it prefers food that is growing rather than cut, perhaps because maple leaves wilt so quickly after being cut. Sleeves should be large and population density small. Cages over young trees would be even better.

Cocoon   The pupa is small, shiny, and dark red-brown.

Adult   This moth is a small one, but with lovely coloring. The base color is dark rich cream. The forewings and hindwings are washed with extremely pale rose, and there are large patches of solid rose on each wing as well. Wingspan about an inch and one quarter. *Rubicunda* is often attracted to light on warm summer evenings.

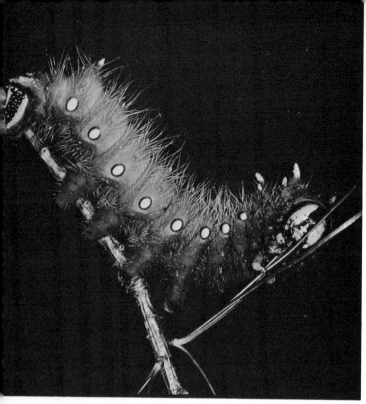

Eacles imperialis Fifth instar larva feeding on pine

Eacles imperialis Pupae

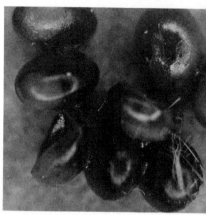

Eacles imperialis The ova are gumm
and stick together. Several of them ar
infertile. The ova are bright yellov
when laid, turning darker just befor
hatching

Eacles imperialis Mounted adult female

EACLES IMPERIALIS

Family   Ceratocampidae

Popular Name   Imperial Moth

Range   The Atlantic Seaboard

Availability   This choice species is much desired by breeders and can be obtained more often from European breeders than from those in this country. Some years it is very scarce. Never too plentiful. Mr. Duke Downey, of Sheridan, Wyoming, often has eggs for sale.

Preferred Foodplant   Pine

Accepted Alternate Foodplants   The list is too long to be put here. The caterpillar could be called almost omnivorous, although I have had best results on Pine. Oak, Maple, Beech, Sycamore, Elm, Cherry, and Sassafras are among other foods known to be accepted.

Diapause   Subterranean pupa

Ova   Large, oval, yellow, and waxy. They are laid in sticky groups.

Larvae   These are beautiful caterpillars, and they have two color phases. The brown phase is not nearly as spectacular as the green one. In the green phase the body is dark yellow-green, covered with short stiff hairs of dark blue-green. The lower half of the body is hunter green. The spiracles are large, bright yellow, and are rimmed first in aqua, then in black. The claspers are gold with a pebbled black central triangle. There are short sharp spines on the body under the hairs, and the thoracic segments bear sets of long sharp deep yellow spines. The head has a black center, orange lobes, and a few freckles of black.

Rearing Requirements   The caterpillars like sunlight and do well sleeved or caged outdoors. They will mature indoors, especially if fed on pine. They are sedentary and do not travel around much, except when they are ready to pupate. Do not crowd them.

Cocoon   The caterpillar goes underground for a considerable distance, so they should be given a deep pupating box. No cocoon, as such, is made, and the pupa is large, fat, dull on the surface and deep brown or black in color. The segments are deeply indented and the antennae cases have several short sharp spines on the bases. The tail is long, flattened, and bifurcated at the extremity, with two minute hooks at either side.

Adult   I remember one afternoon in Irvington, New York. A woman called me and said "Mr. Villiard, the most beautiful butterfly I have ever seen is parked on my stairway." It was a female *imperialis* that had flown to the light on the porch the previous night. She provided me with the first eggs I had been able to obtain of this species. The body color is bright yellow, speckled all over with red-brown freckles. Two small circles of the same color are on each forewing and one on the hindwings. A wavy band, also of the same color, traverses the lower wing and two bands are on the forewings. In the males the forewings are almost covered with the red color, except for a triangle at the tip and a small patch near the bottom edge. Sometimes a female will have the coloring of the male. The wingspan is four inches or more in the female.

Dendrolimus pini Cocoons
spun among Pine twigs

Dendrolimus pini Fifth instar larva feeding on Pine

Dendrolimus pini Ova

Dendrolimus pini Mounted adult female

DENDROLIMUS PINI

Family   Lasiocampidae

Popular Name   Pine Tree Lappet

Range   Europe and possibly England

Availability   European dealers generally offer this species.

Preferred Foodplant   Pine

Accepted Alternate Foodplants   Possibly Hemlock and Spruce

Diapause   Larva

Ova   Smooth, tan ovals. Medium size with a dark red spot on one end and a dark brown spot on the other. Very slightly indented on the sides.

Larvae   Difficult to distinguish from many of the other *Lasiocampid* larvae. Alley cats. Shaggy, hairy, dirty brown-tan, with a few darker markings across the segments on the dorsal surface.

Rearing Requirements   Food. Clean cages, cool airy conditions, and you should have no trouble rearing this species. However, since the caterpillar hibernates throughout the winter, it is imperative to have some sort of protection for them during the intense cold. A good way is to establish them in a cage outdoors, in which plenty of rubble, pine needles, leaves, and similar detritus accumulates on the ground, into which and under which the larvae can find protection. A few rocks piled so as to make small crevices between for shelter spots will help bring the brood through the freezes.

Cocoon   A soft silken cocoon is spun attached to the twig of the foodplant. A few needles or leaf bits are incorporated into the silk to give some strength to the structure, and possibly to serve as added camouflage. The valve end is loosely knit.

Adult   This species has a bit more color variation in the forewings than most of the *Lasiocampidae*. The overall color is dull gray. The hindwings plain. There is a small triangular dark spot in the upper center of the forewing and several shaded, wavy bands of darker color crossing them. Span over two inches.

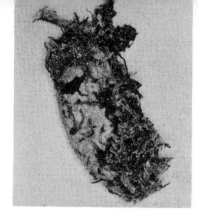

Dendrolimus undans Cocoon
wrapped in sphagnum moss

Dendrolimus undans Fifth instar larva

Dendrolimus undans Ova

Dendrolimus undans Mounted adult male   PHOTO BY RAYMOND OSLAND, ENGLAND

DENDROLIMUS UNDANS

Family Lasiocampidae

Popular Name I do not know of any

Range Indo-Asian Region

Availability Recently the species has become very popular. Available from almost every European breeder and several in the United States as well.

Preferred Foodplant Oak

Accepted Alternate Foodplants Apple

Diapause Egg

Ova Large, rounded ovals. While the body color is cream, the ova are so heavily spotted with dark chestnut as to appear mottled brown. There is a speckled cream ring on one side with a dark brown center, giving the egg the appearance of an eye.

Larvae Long, thin, hairy with the shaggy appearance of an old alley cat. Nondescript coloration of tans and browns, with two black and red patches across the dorsal area on the last two thoracic segments.

Rearing Requirements With all of the *Lasiocampidae,* it is well to remember that they are able to survive our winter weather, and to adapt to whatever foodplant is available—within the limits of their acceptance. Keeping the *Porthetria dispar fiasco* in mind, it is dangerous to rear any *Lasiocampid* unless you are prepared to take really careful steps against the deliberate or accidental liberation or escape of any of the animals. This is not to say that you will start another Gypsy Moth affair, but to remind the beginner that it is within the realm of possibility to do so. *Lasiocampids* are prolific breeders and are tough and sturdy caterpillars. Oak is their preferred food, but Mr. Brian O. C. Gardiner of Cambridge, England, had them take apple. He also had *Kunugia yamadai* accept apple. These are still erroneously known to breeders as *Dendrolimus yamamai,* and they are closely related to *undans.* The caterpillars will accept food that is cut as well as live trees, and will stand crowding to a large degree. When time for pupation arrives a pupating box is welcome, but the larvae will pupate between sheets of newspaper placed in the bottom of their rearing cage, or under layers of dry moss placed in small boxes or in coffee cans.

Cocoon A loose and flimsy silk cocoon is spun under the protecting cover, inside which the very dark pupa is formed. Sometimes bits of moss or dirt are incorporated in the silk of the cocoon, hiding the exterior surface.

Adult All of the interest in rearing *Lasiocampids* is in the larval stage for me, because the adults are very ordinary and have no beauty of color or markings. This one is no exception, being a plain moth of dull brown coloring with a tiny white spot in each forewing and plain dull tannish hindwings. The body is long and tapered and the same color as the hindwings. About two inches or more in span.

Gastropacha populifolia Adult, resting on twig, looks very like a small bird

Gastropacha populifolia Cocoon wrapped in leaves

Gastropacha populifolia Fifth instar larva

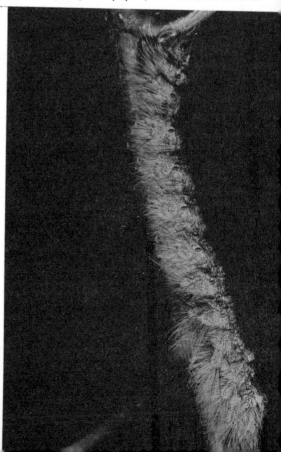

GASTROPACHA POPULIFOLIA

Family   Lasiocampidae

Popular Name   Lappet

Range   Most of Europe, Armenia, Siberia, and the Indo-Asian Region

Availability   I have very seldom seen these offered, and never from domestic breeders. Mr. Robert Gooden of Worldwide Butterflies, Over Compton, England, sent me the only eggs I have ever had of the species.

Preferred Foodplant   Poplar

Accepted Alternate Foodplants   Oak, Elm (see rearing section below), Apple, Sallow, Hawthorn, and others

Diapause   Caterpillar

Ova   Small, oval, beautifully marked with gray mottlings on a cream ground.

Larvae   A flattish very hairy caterpillar of mottled gray color, with no really distinguishing markings on the surface. Tufts of orange hairs spring horizontally from the sides, and there are fleshy "lappets" hanging from the sides which hug the stem as the caterpillar rests upon it, quite hiding the animal by blending in with the color of the twig.

Rearing Requirements   There seems to be a confusion in this species which I have been unable to untangle. Several specific names are in reference books in my library, but none call the species *populifolia*. It seems that G. *quercifolia* is well known and some sort of life history is available on it; G. *ulmifolia* is listed as an aberration, together with a couple of others. These specific names would tend to indicate the preferred foodplants, e.g., elm, oak, or poplar. At any rate, I reared my specimens on poplar with no trouble, and believe they would have accepted willow as well, since nearly every species which accepts one will also accept the other of these two most important foods. I found the caterpillars quiescent during most of the day, becoming more active toward evening. They did not try to find escape openings as much as might be expected of a *Lasiocampid* caterpillar. Normally, when about half grown, the caterpillar goes into its overwintering hibernation at the base of the foodplants. In captivity, however, I kept them going by keeping them warm and supplied with fresh food until they pupated.

Cocoon   The caterpillar spins a long, narrow cocoon of gray-brown silk; it wraps the cocoon in leaves in the rubble at the bottom of the cage, or one or two may spin their cocoons attached to the stems of the foodplants. The pupa is dark brown and covered with a sticky white powder, much like the pupa of *Catocalas*.

Adult   A queer little moth that looks for all the world like a little bird perched on a branch. The forewings are held folded up over the body, and are crenulate on their edges, giving the appearance of feathers on the back of the bird. The head is long and projected in front until it very strongly resembles the beak. The wings are a plain pale red-brown, with a few darker speckles all over them. One larger speckle is so positioned as to make the eye of the bird. A truly remarkable resemblance. Span about two inches or a little more.

Kunugia (Dendrolimus) yamadai Secor instar larva

Kunugia (Dendrolimus) yamadai Fifth instar larva

Kunugia (Dendrolimus) yamadai Ova

Kunugia (Dendrolimus) yamadai Mounted adult male
PHOTO BY RAYMOND OSLAND, ENGLAND

KUNUGIA YAMADAI (DENDROLIMUS YAMADAI, D. YAMAMAI)

Family Lasiocampidae

Popular Name I know of none

Range Indo-Asian Region

Availability This is one of the species of Japanese moths which have become very popular in the last few years. Almost every dealer has eggs in season, especially European breeders. Known under several names.

Preferred Foodplant Oak

Accepted Alternate Foodplants Chestnut, Pine, Hawthorn, and Apple

Diapause Egg

Ova Quite large, oval, and smooth. The ground color is cream, but the eggs are so heavily covered with dark chestnut markings as to appear brown. On the side is the micropyle, a black dot surrounded by cream. A very large chestnut spot is on one end; it also is surrounded by cream, giving the egg the appearance of being an eyeball. A group of ova look like an assortment of dolls' eyes.

Larvae This species is no exception to most of the *Lasiocampidae*—it looks just like an alley cat. The body is splotchy black and white. There is a hairy mop extending from the first five segments. The rest of the body is covered with shorter brushes of untidy hairs, from which an occasional long hair straggles upward.

Rearing Requirements This caterpillar seems to go on forever. It has innumerable molts and I have had them continue to eat from early spring well into the fall! They are restless explorers, always prowling around their cage. They like a lot of rubble in the bottom of the cage in which they spin their cocoon.

Cocoon Flimsy, spun up in leaves or rubble, with hairs from the body incorporated in the silk. The adults emerge in the fall and lay their eggs which overwinter.

Adult Nothing much to look at. It is more or less typical of the *Lasiocampid* moths. The body and wings are a sandy-tan color, with faint and obscure lines or markings. The body is heavy and covered with long hairs. The scales are not very firmly attached to the wing surfaces, and brush off very easily if the moth is handled. Care must be taken in mounting specimens to avoid denuding the wings.

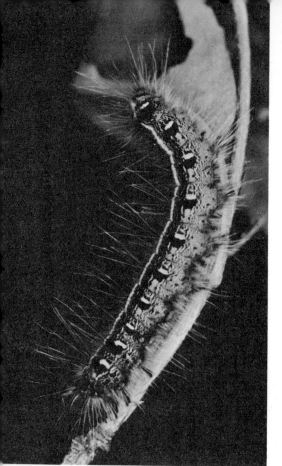

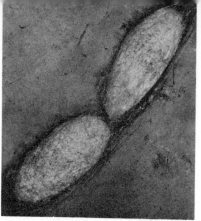

Malacosoma americana Cocoons spun up under the ledge of a flower pot

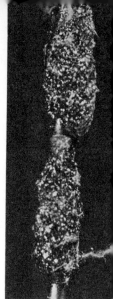

Malacosoma amer
Two hatched ring
eggs on a twig of
Cherry

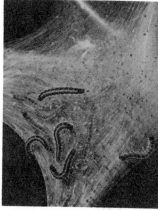

Malacosoma americana Fifth instar larva

Malacosoma americana A "tent" with second instar larvae

Malacosoma americana Mounted adult female

MALACOSOMA AMERICANA

Family   Lasiocampidae

Popular Name   Tent Caterpillar

Range   The Appalachian Subregion

Availability   Certainly not one to be found in dealers' stocks. This one can be found in any quantity all over the northeastern States in the spring when their tents disfigure the trees.

Preferred Foodplant   Wild Cherry

Accepted Alternate Foodplants   Apple, Plum, and many other fruit trees

Diapause   Ova

Ova   Laid in tight rings around the twigs of the foodplants.

Larvae   Hardly any description needs be made of this familiar scourge of our orchards. Taken individually, however, the caterpillar is very pretty. The body is pale blue, and two broken orange stripes run along the tops and the bottoms of the spiracles, which are white with a black patch against their rearward edges. There is a white stripe on the dorsal surface bordered by black and orange stripes. The entire body is covered with short brown hairs. Urticating to some persons, but not to everyone.

Rearing Requirements   While rearing *americanus* is not generally done in captivity—the emphasis is usually on exterminating the species—still they are easily cared for if you get them in the first or second instar or as eggs. They require a large cage and a heavy branch of the foodplant, because the gregarious colony makes a web of silk in the crotch, foraging from it to feed. As they leave the web in the morning they travel to the outermost tip of the branches, laying a silken trail as they go. After spending the day feeding, they follow the trail back to the web for the night. As they grow and enter the new instars, the web is enlarged to accommodate them. When pupating time arrives, the entire colony leaves the web to travel all over the surrounding area to make their cocoons under rocks, on fence rails, under any overhanging protection, or among roots of the low growing plants.

Cocoon   Fuzzy white cocoons are made anywhere it is protected. The cocoon is small, elongated, and soft. Often many are made in a group, overlapping one another. The moth emerges in the fall to mate and deposit its eggs.

Adult   A small moth, dun colored with faint white lines dividing the forewings. The hindwings are plain dun color with no markings. A narrow white edge borders the wings. The body is the same color. Span a little over an inch.

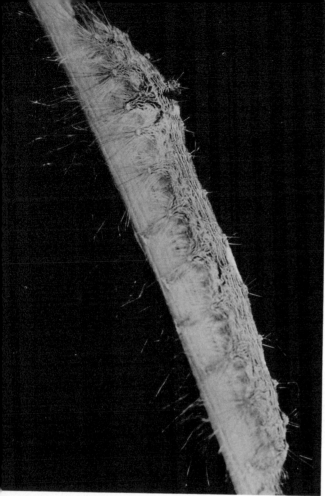

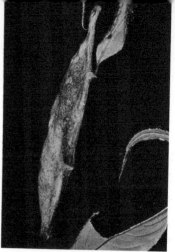

Tolype velleda Cocoon

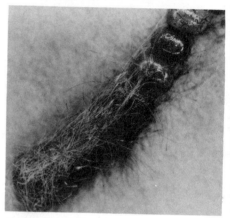

Tolype velleda Fifth instar larva

Tolype velleda Ova, partly depilated
to show egg placement under hairs

Tolype velleda Mounted adult male

TOLYPE VELLEDA

Family   Lasiocampidae

Popular Name   None to my knowledge

Range   Appalachian region of the United States

Availability   Offered by American breeders every few seasons.

Preferred Foodplant   Willow

Accepted Alternate Foodplants   Lilac, Sallow

Diapause   Cocoon

Ova   The eggs of this moth are very curious. The female lays them in slightly curved rows of ten to a dozen or more; then, utilizing the long gray hairs from her abdomen, she covers the row completely—giving it the appearance of a caterpillar. The eggs themselves are fairly large, speckled brown, oval with a depression in the side.

Larvae   The caterpillar of *velleda* is typical of most of the *Lasiocampidae*, flattish, hairy, and a nondescript mottled gray in color. This one has a fringe of long hairs on the sides, so that, when lying along a twig, the prolegs are covered and almost hidden from view.

Rearing Requirements   Nothing special. The caterpillars take a long time to mature, in common with many of their relatives. They feed slowly, and growth is erratic, increasing in spurts with long periods of dormancy between molts.

Cocoon   A small tight cocoon is spun attached to a twig of the foodplant. The cocoon is long and pointed at both ends, and several are often spun overlapping each other when the larvae are cage reared.

Adult   The sexes are very much alike, about the only difference being the color of the "cape" over the thorax: in the female it is thick and white, while in the male it is somewhat more sparse and tan in color. The body of the female, especially, is covered with long hairs which are used to conceal the rows of eggs as they are laid. This is a small moth, with a span of about two inches. The wings are gray with three bars of white running across the forewings.

Bombyx mori Larval group on Mulberry leaves

Bombyx mori Cocoon, with adult pair in copul on top of it

Bombyx mori Ova

Bombyx mori Mounted adult male

BOMBYX MORI

Family Bombycidae

Popular Name Silkworm

Range Originally indigenous to China

Availability B. mori is now to be found in almost every country in the world, but in confinement only. It is not available in the wild state. Almost any dealer can supply eggs in season.

Preferred Foodplant Mulberry

Accepted Alternate Foodplants Mori is said to take Lettuce, but I have never heard of any breeder successfully rearing them on anything other than Mulberry.

Ova Small, dirty white, flattened rounds, turning dark when fertile.

Larvae Naked, gray-white, somewhat like suet. An ugly caterpillar, and one reared mainly because of its great commercial value. There is a stubby horn on the anal segment, and some larvae have a wash of pale brown on the three or four anterior segments.

Rearing Requirements Rearing silkworms is not too difficult, albeit somewhat of a nuisance. After five thousand years of breeding in captivity, these caterpillars have become so dependent on being hand-reared that they would starve to death if put out wild. They are so helpless that they do not need to be confined in cages—they will not leave the leaf they are feeding upon. Indeed, they do not even look for another leaf after having finished one, but merely wait for one to drop on top of it—a kind of "manna from heaven" idea. Any shallow pan will do to rear a brood in. Simply keep a supply of fresh leaves cut from the branches without stems. As the ones in the tray are consumed, lay new ones on top of the larva. Empty the frass from time to time during the day and the caterpillars are perfectly contented. Keep indoors and sheltered from drafts.

Cocoon When ready to pupate the larva empties its gut in the fashion of all caterpillars, then wanders slightly looking for a crevice. If an empty egg box is offered, the caterpillars will spin in the cavities. If you rear them for the silk, the pupa must be killed while within the cocoon, otherwise the silk will be ruined when the moth emerges from the cocoon.

Adult Since the mating takes place almost immediately upon emergence—most often even before the wings have been expanded—in order to obtain a perfect specimen for mounting it is best to remove a single moth and confine it until it expands and dries. It is not at all uncommon to find two males with wet draggled wings mating the same female whose wings are in a similar condition. Right after mating the female lays her eggs by the hundred in patches all over the cocoon, the foodplant, or wherever she happens to be sitting. Small, dirty creamy white, no distinguishing markings to speak of, this is a completely uninteresting specimen, but one that cannot be overlooked in human economy. About an inch or better in span.

Endromis versicolora Mounted adult female

Endromis versicolora Third instar larvae in typical fensive posture on twig. The larvae congregate in groups and spit green fluid when disturbed

Endromis versicolora Ova laid on twig

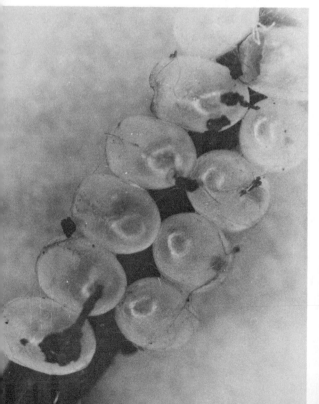

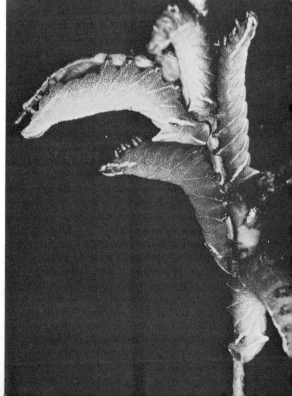

ENDROMIS VERSICOLORA

Family   Endromidae

Popular Name   Kentish Glory (in England)

Range   British Isles and Central Europe

Availability   Generally available in Europe

Preferred Foodplant   Birch

Accepted Alternate Foodplants   Alder and Lime (*Tilia*) are sometimes accepted

Diapause   Cocoon

Ova   The eggs are medium sized and yellow-green when first deposited and turn dark purple-brown after a few days if fertile. Otherwise they remain greenish.

Larvae   The caterpillars of *versicolora* are curious, indeed, in their habit of congregating in dense groups around the extremities of the branch upon which they are feeding. At the slightest disturbance they all bend their bodies out from the branch and remain rigidly curved, much like a bunch of flower petals. They also spit, much like a grasshopper ejects "tobacco juice."

Rearing Requirements   Nothing special. I have had no success with any food other than birch, but many breeders in Europe have reared this species on lime and alder. They do want fresh leaves, and the birch should be changed twice daily if cage reared.

Cocoon   The caterpillars spin a coarse, somewhat flimsy, cocoon on the surface of the ground among dead leaves and bits of moss. The pupa within the meshed cocoon is dull, rough on the surface, and dark brown in color.

Adult   This is a pretty species, with cryptic coloration of the wings, which are red-brown with many white triangles and dark wavy lines running across the forewings. The hindwings also have the wavy lines which, when the moth is mounted, becomes a continuous line with those of the forewings. The female is considerably paler than the male, and is also larger.

Syntomeida epilais Mounted adult male

Syntomeida epilais Cocoon and pupae. The dark spotted
pupa is ready to emerge

Syntomeida epilais Fifth instar larva

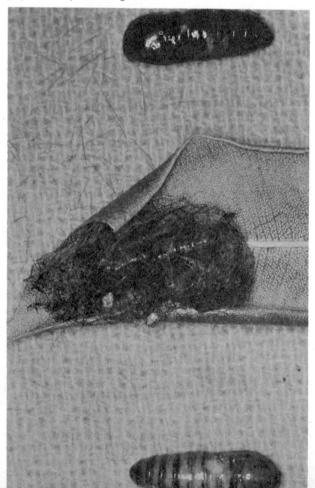

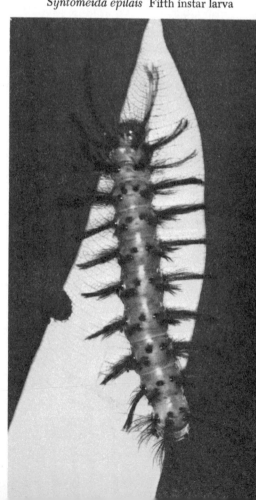

SYNTOMEIDA EPILAIS

Family   Syntomidae

Popular Name   Polka Dot Moth, Polka Dot Wasp Moth

Range   Southern United States around the Gulf of Mexico

Availability   I have never seen this species offered for sale by American breeders, except by myself in 1964, from stock taken in Florida in the spring of that year. They are, however, easily taken in the larval stage in the wild habitat.

Preferred Foodplant   Oleander

Accepted Alternate Foodplants   None to my knowledge

Diapause   This species seems to be continuously brooded in its habitat, with no seasonal diapause.

Ova   Small round green-yellow, laid singly on the leaves of the foodplant.

Larvae   A striking creature, with the body a bright brick red, covered with tufts of long stiff black hairs.

Rearing Requirements   About the only thing I have found *epilais* to want is plenty of warmth; it languishes in cool temperatures. The foodplant should be fresh—the caterpillars seem to prefer the leaves when they are succulent and juicy. The juice of the Oleander is poisonous if swallowed, and children should not be allowed to handle the plants, especially half-eaten leaves which may still be exuding the sap.

Cocoon   A thin cocoon is spun up in a curled leaf of the foodplant, utilizing weak silk and the black hairs from the body of the caterpillar.

Adult   A beautiful little creature, this moth is the mimic of a wasp. Its body is slender and wasp-shaped. The wings and body are a gleaming metallic blue-black with enamel-white spots on both. At the tip of the abdomen the body is deep brick color. About one-and-one-half-inch span.

Hemerocampa leucostigma Mounted adult female

Hemerocampa leucostigma These larvae may be found in considerable numbers on low Oaks. Their bright colors and bristly appearance make them quite noticeable

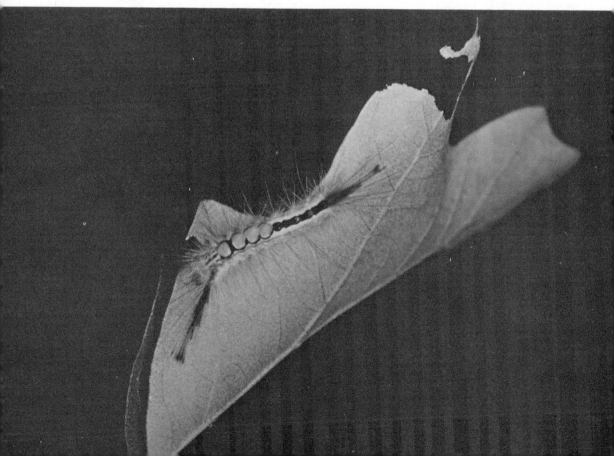

HEMEROCAMPA LEUCOSTIGMA

Family   Liparidae

Popular Name   White-marked Tussock Moth

Range   The Appalachian subregion

Availability   Seldom, if ever, offered by breeders. It is too easy to find the larvae in the wild state.

Preferred Foodplant   Oak

Accepted Alternate Foodplants   Almost omnivorous. All deciduous trees and shrubs.

Diapause   The second or third generation egg

Ova   Very small, round, pale. Laid on the cocoon.

Larvae   Despite the disapprobation in which this species is held, it remains that the caterpillar is really one of our more beautiful ones, and an easy one to rear. For the experience of breeding, it is an excellent choice for the beginner, who should, however, dispose of his stock in any other way than the release of it to the wilds, since, unfortunately, the country is already lavishly populated with what can only be called a pest. There are several points of interest with this species. For one thing, the sexes are readily distinguishable in the larval stage, which is not the case with most caterpillars. The male of *leucostigma* is half the size of the female, and is therefore easily identified. The same disparity of size is evidenced in the pupae. The head is vermillion and the body is white with black stripes. Stiff tufts of white hairs stand out from the sides and four short straight groups of bristles very like those on a toothbrush stand erect on the dorsal surface of the third, fourth, fifth, and sixth segments. One long black group of bristles points rearward and two more diverge forward from the front end.

Rearing Requirements   This is one species which will accept drying leaves; although the caterpillars will reject the leaves if they are really sere, they need not be as succulent as those needed for most other caterpillars. Oak leaves, which are stiff and hard, are readily eaten. The small heads of the caterpillars enable them to escape through tiny openings, so care should be taken to keep them in secure quarters.

Cocoon   The cocoons are fuzzy with the hairs from the bodies of the animals and are fastened to the twigs of the foodplants, or may be spun up in a crevice of bark or under a stone.

Adult   The female of *leucostigma* is wingless and looks like a fat grub. She emerges from the cocoon but does not travel very far away. The mating takes place almost immediately upon emergence and she lays her eggs in a mat on the surface of the cocoon. The male is nondescript, small—about an inch to an inch and one half in span; plain brown wings with faint obscure markings.

Porthetria dispar Mounted adult female

Porthetria dispar It is not at all uncommon to find a pupating caterpillar, empty pupal case, and a patch of eggs all together on the underside of a rock

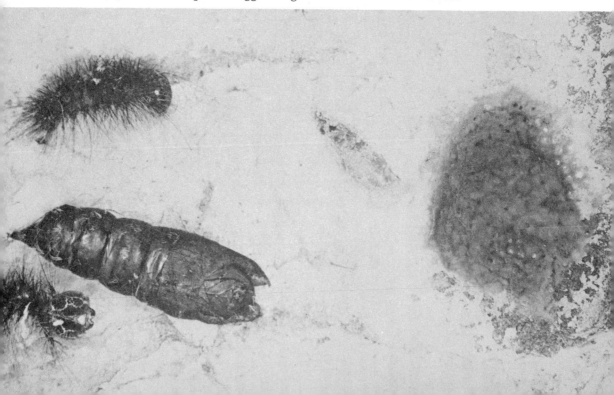

PORTHETRIA DISPAR

Family   Liparidae

Popular Name   Gypsy Moth

Range   Introduced and now covering the New England States

Availability   Certainly no breeder in his right mind would offer eggs of this species. Just drive through New England any fall and pick a few thousand off the trunks of any tree, rock, fence post, or other support.

Preferred Foodplant   Anything

Accepted Alternate Foodplants   Any kind of tree, shrub, weed, or plant

Diapause   Egg patches

Ova   Laid in patches, then covered with the hairs from the body of the female. The familiar patches are dark cream and stuck on the trunks of trees or any convenient support, generally with the empty pupal cases hanging in clusters nearby.

Larvae   Not a bad looking caterpillar. The body is gray covered with long soft brown hairs. The first five segments carry a pair of blue protuberances on the dorsal surface, and those on the remainder of the segments are brick red. The head has two black spots looking like big eyes. Very gregarious.

Rearing Requirements   Just be careful that you do not release any of these animals if you breed them. They are a real scourge in our forests and parks, since there do not seem to be enough natural predators in our country to keep them in check. Curiously enough, the species is almost extinct in Great Britain, and I have had many requests to ship them eggs in order that they may re-establish a race there. So far, this attempt has met with little success!

Cocoon   *Dispar* makes a naked pupa hanging in clusters from any convenient support. The pupae are as gregarious as the caterpillar and sometimes literally hundreds can be seen in a bunch. The moths emerge in the early fall or late summer and the female lays her egg patches near the place of emergence.

Adult   The males are darker than the females. In the latter, the wings are almost white and there are dark brown or black wavy lines and spots adorning the forewings. The hindwings are solid white with a row of small dark spots on the margins. The male is marked the same except that the ground color is brown and the marginal spots on the hindwings are white. Span about one and one-half inches.

Appendix I

WINTER TWIGS

In this appendix a group of winter terminal twigs are pictured in their most recognizable condition so you may identify foodplants in the winter or early spring in order to have them available for early-hatching eggs. Often, especially in the case of some of the African and Asian exotic species, the eggs arrive either in the fall or in the very early part of the year, and hatch out long before the buds have opened on our native trees and shrubs.

When this happens, the only recourse is to cut branches of the foodplant and bring them inside for forcing in the warmth of the room. This is a regular practice of nurserymen, who want trees and shrubs in full foliage for early flower shows. Of course, it is far better if you can bring a growing plant inside rather than cut branches, but even branches can be forced to the point where the buds are developed enough to open slightly, which is all that is necessary in order to get your tiny caterpillars started.

Branches should be cut at intervals of two to three days, and started in water at those intervals, in order to have a continuing supply of food until the leaves open in the wild. One well-started branch would be enough to start your hatchlings on for the first day, and possibly for the second and third days, too. Then two branches should be offered, increasing the amount of food by the amount of growth attained by the animals and by their appetite. It is not necessary to cut whole bundles of food to force, since the feeding is done at a time when the larvae are tiny and have corresponding appetites. Just make sure you do not run short, since it takes several days to start buds indoors, and the caterpillars would starve to death if they ran out and had to wait for newly started food.

If the buds are small or tight, they may be gently picked open with the aid of a fine needle or one of your spreading needles and a magnifying glass; take care not to tear the tiny leaves apart or they will die. In the case of some of the small Japanese species, and, of course, species from other parts of the world, too, the eggs can be placed on a bud, and, after hatching, the caterpillar will make its way into the heart of the bud and feed there out of sight for several days.

Red Maple–Swamp Maple
Acer rubrum

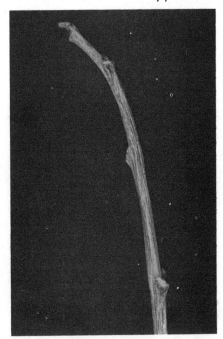

Pawpaw–Papaw
Asimina triloba

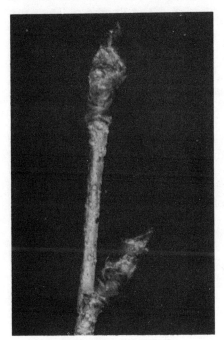

White Birch–*Betula alba*

Paper Birch–Canoe Birch
Betula papyrifera

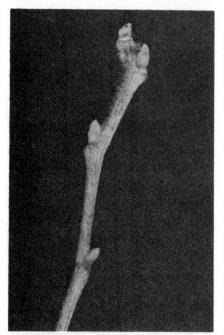

Chestnut—*Castanea dentata*

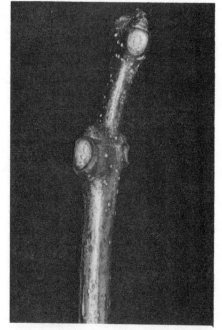

Catalpa—Bean Tree—Cigar Tree
Catalpa bignonioides

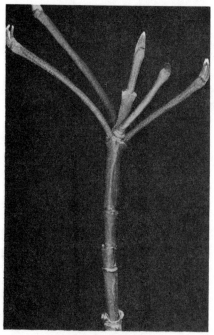

Dogwood—Boxwood
Cornus florida

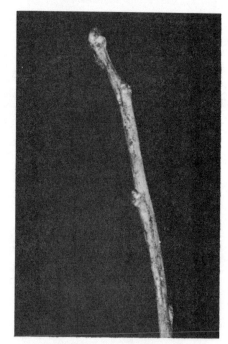

Hawthorn—Washington Thorn
Crataegus phaenopyrum

Russian Olive—Oleaster
Elaeagnus angustifolia

Copper Beech—*Fagus sylvatica cuprea*

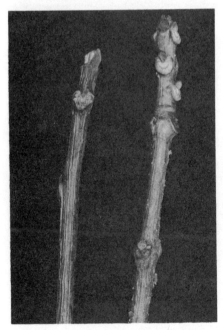

Green Ash—*Fraxinus pennsylvanica*

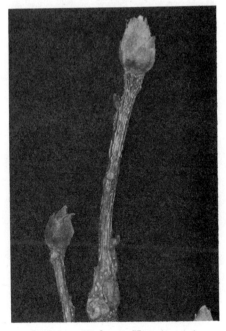

Bitternut Hickory—*Hicoria minima*

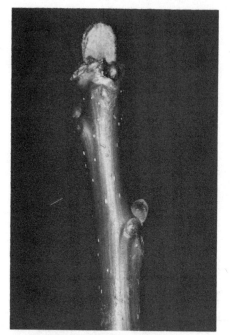

English Walnut—Butternut
Juglans cinerea

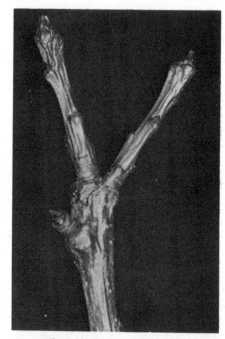

Black Walnut—*Juglans nigra*

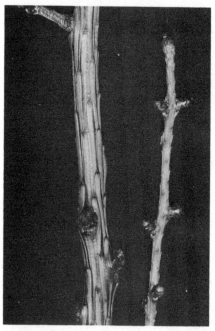

American Larch—Tamarack—Hackmatack
Larix laricina

Privet—*Ligustrum ovalifolia*

Tulip-Tree—Whitewood—Tulip Poplar—
Yellow Poplar *Liriodendron tulipifera*

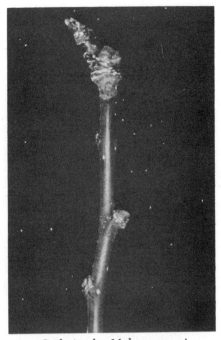

Crab Apple—*Malus coronaria*

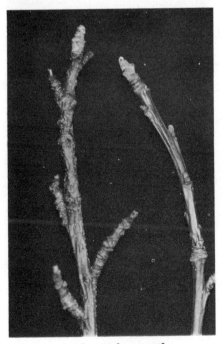

Apple—*Malus pumila*

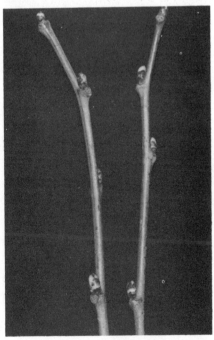

White Mulberry—*Morus alba*

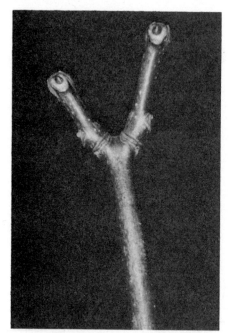

Phellodendron—Cork Tree
Phellodendron amurense

White Poplar—*Populus alba*

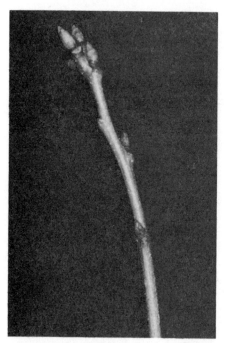

Aspen—Large-toothed Aspen *Populus grandidentata*

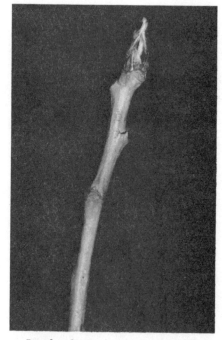

Lombardy Poplar—*Populus nigra italica*

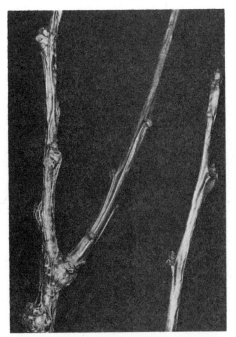

Apricot—*Prunus ameniaca*

Plum (Fellenberg Prune)—*Prunus domestica*

Beach Plum—*Prunus maritima*

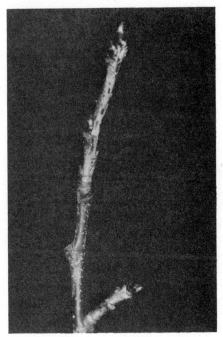

Wild Cherry—Bird Cherry   *Prunus pennsylvanica*

Wild Pear—Japanese Pear
Pyrus pyrifolia

Scrub Oak—Bear Oak   *Quercus ilicifolia—Quercus nana*

Post Oak—*Quercus minor*

Pin Oak—*Quercus palustris*

Mountain Sumac—*Rhus cismontana*

Smooth Sumac—*Rhus glabra*

Stagshorn Sumac—*Rhus typhina*

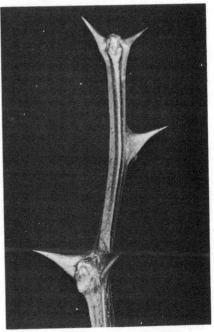

Black Locust—False Acacia—Yellow
Locust—*Robinia pseudo-acacia*

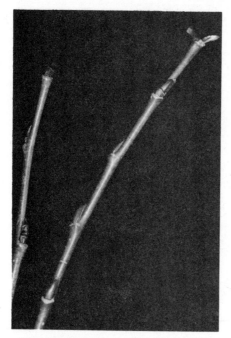

Black Willow—*Salix nigra*

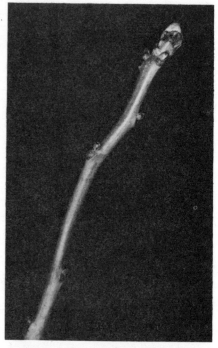

Sassafras—*Sassafras albidum*

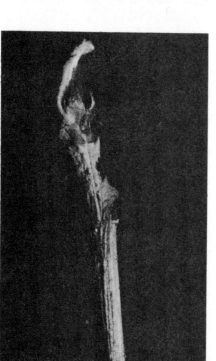

Mountain Ash—*Sorbus americana*

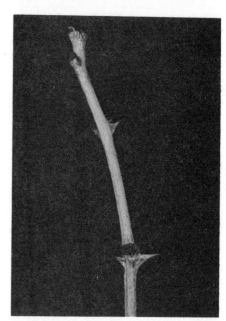

Prickley Ash—Toothache Tree
Zanthoxylum americanum

Japanese Elm—Zelkova—*Zelkova serrata*

Appendix II

GUIDE TO FOODPLANTS

Here is a handy ready-reference guide to foodplants. An assortment of moths are listed, with many of the foodplants known to be accepted noted after each name. To save time reading through the life histories, you can instantly determine if you would be able to rear any given moth simply by running down the list until you find the species in question, then looking to see if you have the foodplant available. If you have the chance to obtain eggs of *Hyalophora columbia*, for instance, but have no Larch, and no way to get any, then, patently, it would be useless to order or accept the eggs, since the hatched caterpillars would merely languish and die for lack of their specific foodplant. For this reason, as many alternate foodplants as I have been able to locate are offered here for your convenience:

ACTIAS ARTEMIS.
Apple, Apricot, Black Alder, Cherry, Maple, Pear, Plum, Birch, Pomegranate.

ACTIAS SELENE.
Apple, Cherry, Moorwort (*Andromeda glaucophylla*), Rhododendron, Walnut, Willow.

AGLIA TAU.
Birch, Beech, Black Alder, Chestnut, Linden, Maple, Oak.

AMORPHA POPULI.
Aspen, Birch, Laurel, Laurustinus (*Viburnum tinus*), Poplar, Willow.

ANISOTA SENATORIA.
Oak.

ANTHERAEA ASSAMENSIS (A. ASSAMI).
Oak, Apple, Live Oak.

ANTHERAEA MYLITTA.
Oak, Beech, Hornbeam, Plum.

ANTHERAEA PAPHIA.
Oak.

ANTHERAEA PERNYI.
Apple, Oak.

ANTHERAEA YAMAMAI.
Oak, Chestnut, Apple, Beech, Hickory, Plum, Mulberry.

APATELODES TORREFACTA.
Cherry.

ARCTIA CAJA.
Dandelion, Plantain, Lettuce, Dock, Nettle, Strawberry, Hollyhock, Cabbage, Mulberry, Radish.

ARGEMA MITTREI.
Poison Ivy, Pepper Tree (*Schinus molle*), *Eugenia cuneifolia*, Mimosa, *Weinmannia eriocampa*.

ATTACUS ATLAS (ALL SPECIES).
Lilac, Ash, Sassafras, Privet, Ailanthus, Cherry, Rhododendron, Mountain Laurel.

AUTOMERIS AURANTIACA.
Privet, Lilac, Willow, Wild Cherry, and possibly others.

AUTOMERIS IO.
Corn, Wild Cherry, Lilac, Willow, Sassafras, Privet, Lime (*Tilia*), Hawthorn, Poplar, Box Elder, Elm, Cotton.

AUTOMERIS LEUCANE.
Birch, Wild Cherry, Lilac, Privet, Plum, Apple, Black Locust.

BOMBYX MORI.
Mulberry, Lettuce.

BRAHMAEA JAPONICA.
Lilac, Ash, Privet.

BRAHMAEA WALLICHI.
Fragrant Olive, Mignonette, Privet, Lilac, Willow, Spindle Tree, Holly.

BUNEA ALCINOE.
Sumac (*Rhus glabra*), Rose, Plum, Hawthorn, Apple, Cherry.

CALIGULA BOISDUVALI.
Oak, Chestnut, Maple, Zelkova, Acacia, Walnut, Cherry, Plum, Pear, Mountain Ash, Crab Apple.

CALLOSAMIA PROMETHEA.
Lilac, Wild Cherry, Sassafras, Privet, Ash, Willow, Tulip Tree, Poplar, Spicebush, Sweet Gum, Button Bush, Maple, Basswood, Barberry, Birch, Prunus species.

CALLOSYMBOLUS MYOPS.
Wild Cherry, Willow, Poplar.

CATOCALA CONCUMBENS.
Willow, Poplar.

CATOCALA FRAXINI.
Ash, Oak, Poplar, Willow.

CATOCALA NUPTA.
Willow, Poplar, Hackberry.

CELERIO EUPHORBIAE.
Spurge cyprissa, Sea Spurge, Fuchsia, Oak.

CELERIO LINEATA.
Purslane (*Portulaca*), Virginia Creeper, Grape.

CERATOMIA AMYNTOR.
Elm, Locust, Willow, Ash, Linden.

CERURA SCITISCRIPTA.
Poplar, Willow.

CERURA VINULA.
Sallow, Willow, Poplar, Apple, Ash, Plum, Hops.

CITHERONIA BRISSOTTII.
Walnut.

CITHERONIA REGALIS.
Smooth Sumac (*Rhus glabra*), Willow, Oak, Hickory, Walnut, Shining Sumac (*Rhus copallina*), Mountain Sumac (*Rhus cismontana*).

CITHERONIA SPLENDENS.
Walnut, Hickory, Pecan, Butternut.

CRICULA ANDREI.
Privet, Hawthorn, Plum.

DARAPSA MYRON.
Ampelopsis (Pepper Vine and others), Wild Grape, Virginia Creeper.

DEIDAMIA INSCRIPTUM.
Wild Grape, Virginia Creeper.

DENDROLIMUS PINI.
Pine.

DENDROLIMUS UNDANS.
Oak, Chestnut, Pine.

DICTYOPLOCA JAPONICA.
Walnut, Lacquer Tree (*Schleichera trijuga*), Wax Tree (*Rhus verniciflus*), Zelkova, Oak, Chestnut, Maple, Cherry, Plum, Peach, Apricot, Camphor Tree (*Cinnamomum camphora*), Crepe Myrtle, Plane Tree, Judas Tree (*Cercis siliquastrum*), Apple, Hawthorn, Willow.

DICTYOPLOCA SIMLA.
Walnut, Birch, Oak, Hickory, Willow, Pear, Apple, Hawthorn.

DIRPHIA CURITIBA.
Walnut, Oak.

DRYOCAMPA RUBICUNDA.
Maple.

EACLES IMPERIALIS.
Maple, Sassafras, Box Elder, Pine, Beech, Hickory, Oak, Sumac, and others.

ENDROMIS VERSICOLORA.
Birch, Hazel.

ESTIGMENE ACRAEA.
Oleander, Sea Grape, Dandelion, Dock, Plantain, and almost anything else in the low-growing weeds.

EUPACKARDIA CALETTA.
Senecio, Acacia, Wild Cherry, Privet, Ash, Willow, Pepper Tree, Birch, Plum, and many others.

EUPARTHENOS NUBILIS.
Poplar, Willow, Linden, Locust.

GASTROPACHA POPULIFOLIA.
Poplar, Willow.

HEMEROCAMPA LEUCOSTIGMA.
Oak, almost omnivorous, accepting all deciduous trees.

HEMILEUCA MAIA.
Willow, Oak, Wild Cherry, Poplar, Hazel.

HEMILEUCA NEVADENSIS.
Willow, Oak, Cherry, Hazel.

HYALOPHORA CECROPIA.
Lilac, Wild Cherry, Willow, Ozier, Plum, Apple, Maple, Alder, Pecan, Buttonbush, Elderberry, Box Elder.

HYALOPHORA COLUMBIA.
Larch.

HYALOPHORA GLOVERI.
Lilac, Willow, Wild Cherry, Ozier, Privet, Alder, Maple, Wild Currant, Choke Cherry, Buffalo Berry, Prunus species.

HYALOPHORA EURYALIS (H. RUBRA).
Lilac, Wild Cherry, Ozier, Willow, Plum, Apple, Maple, Manzanita, California Coffee-Berry, Mountain Birch, Prunus species, Pepper Tree (*Schinus molle*), Buttonbush, Ceanothus.

HYLOICUS GORDIUS.
Dogwood, Crab Apple, Ozier, Rosaceae.

HYLOICUS KALMIAE.
Mountain Laurel, Privet, Lilac, Ash.

HYLOICUS PINASTRI.
Pine.

ISIA ISABELLA.
Dandelion, Plantain, Dock, and other weeds and grasses.

KUNUGIA YAMADAI.
Oak, Chestnut, Pine, Hawthorn, Apple.

LOEPA KATINKA.
Virginia Creeper, Grape, Hawthorn.

MALACOSOMA AMERICANA.
Wild Cherry, Plum, Apple.

NOTODONTA ZICZAC.
Sallow, Poplar, Willow.

NUDAURELIA CYTHERAEA.
Pine, Larch, Rose, Sumac (*Rhus glabra*).

PACHYSPHINX MODESTA.
Poplar, Willow.

PANTHEA COENOBITA.
Pine.

PHALERA BUCEPHALA.
Lime (*Tilia*), Oak, Hazel, Elm, Wild Plum, Alder, Willow, Sallow, Maple, and other trees.

PORTHETRIA DISPAR.
Almost completely omnivorous. Will accept any tree or shrub.

PSEUDOHAZIS HERA.
Sagebrush.

PYROPHILA PYRAMIDOIDES.
Grape, Rhododendron, various shrubs.

RHODINIA FUGAX.
Chestnut, Oak, Black Alder, Hackberry, Cherry, Maple, Plum, Sycamore.

ROTHSCHILDIA JACOBAEA.
Privet.

ROTHSCHILDIA ORIZABA.
Privet, Lilac, Buttonbush, Ash, Sassafras, Willow, Pepper Tree (*Schinus molle*), Cherry, Plum, Apricot, and others.

ROTHSCHILDIA SPECULIFERA.
Cherry, Lilac, Buttonbush, Ash, Privet.

SAMIA CYNTHIA.
Ailanthus, Lilac, Sassafras, Ash, Castor Bean, Cherry, Willow, and other deciduous trees.

SATURNIA PAVONIA.
Rose, Raspberry, Hawthorn, Apple, Whitethorn, Blackthorn, Heather, Plum, Sallow, Purple Loosestrife, Willow, Alder, Meadow Sweet (*Spirea alba*), Ash, Hops.

SATURNIA PYRI.

Ash, Privet, Cherry, Birch, Pear, Apple, Plum, Hops, Horse Chestnut, Lime (*Tilia*), Elm, Poplar, Almond.

SMERINTHUS OCELLATA.

Sallow, Poplar, Willow, Sloe, Lime (*Tilia*), Apple, Pear, Peach, Almond.

SMERINTHUS PLANUS.

Red Ozier, Poplar, Ash, Birch.

SPHECODINA ABBOTTI.

Virginia Creeper, Grape.

SPHINX LIGUSTRI.

Privet, Ash, Lilac, Holly, Laurestinus (*Viburnum tinus*).

SYNTOMEIDA EPILAIS.

Oleander, Sea Grape.

TELEA POLYPHEMUS.

Oak, Birch, Elm, Linden, Maple, Chestnut, Cherry, Plum, Willow, Ozier, Apple, Hawthorn.

TOLYPE VELLEDA.

Willow, Lilac, Sallow.

TROPEA LUNA.

Hickory, Walnut, Birch, Oak, Willow, Butternut, Sweet Gum, Persimmon, Pecan.

Index